CONTENTS

ONLINE ACTIVITIES

On some of the pages you will see QR codes. These QR codes take you to online Purple Mash activities which support learning from the relevant page.

To use the QR codes, scan the QR code with the camera on your web enabled tablet, click on the link and the activity will appear on screen.

Alternatively, QR readers are available on the app store for your device.

SCAN CODE

purple mash

Published 2022. Little Brother Books Ltd, Ground Floor, 23 Southernhay East, Exeter, Devon EX1 1QL
books@littlebrotherbooks.co.uk | www.littlebrotherbooks.co.uk
Printed in the United Kingdom.
The Little Brother Books trademark, email and website addresses, are the sole and exclusive properties of Little Brother Books Limited.

LB BOOKS

NUMBERS TO 10,000,000

Lana Loud wants to help her neighbours cut down on energy use but she needs to read their electricity meters first. Her smart sister, Lisa, has created a table to help remind her what each value is worth.

1 Write down the value of the digits highlighted in **red**. The first one has been done for you.

M	HTh	TTh	Th	H	T	O	Value of red digit
Millions	Hundred Thousands	Ten Thousands	Thousands	Hundreds	Tens	Ones	
2	3	**6**	3	2	0	1	60,000
1	**1**	4	1	5	1	3	
5	6	0	8	**7**	9	7	
5	1	8	4	3	9	1	
3	1	0	**7**	0	1	5	
4	4	8	6	8	3	**9**	

2 Now help Lana write down written numbers in figures. The first one has been done for you.

a. Five million, six hundred and fifty five thousand, three hundred and forty five.

> 5,655,345

b. Nine million, eight hundred and eight thousand, three hundred and eleven.

c. Two million, four hundred and forty six thousand, six hundred and fifty one.

d. One million, seven hundred and twenty nine thousand and four.

e. Nine Million, nine hundred and nine thousand, nine hundred.

ROUNDING NUMBERS

SCAN CODE

Athletic Lynn is super good at sport. Help her round the scores from her latest successes up or down.

If the key number is a <u>5</u> you need to round up.

5<u>5</u> rounded to the nearest 10 becomes 60.

1,<u>5</u>79 rounded to the nearest 1,000 becomes 2,000.

1 Lynn has rounded some of her scores to the nearest 10 but has forgotten which one goes with which. Can you draw lines from the number to the nearest 10?

45	90
32	30
91	40
35	50
75	80

2 Draw a circle around all the numbers that will be rounded to 300 to the nearest hundred.

256   377

398

309   299

3 Draw a circle around all the numbers that will be rounded to 8,000 to the nearest thousand.

8,888   8,808

8,008

8,080   8,401

4 Draw a circle around all the numbers that will be rounded to 50,000 to the nearest ten thousand..

49,356   56,651

45,001

59,090   48,743

5

a. The number 55 rounded to the nearest 10 is [ ] and to the nearest 100 is [ ].

b. The number 644 rounded to the nearest 100 is [ ] and to the nearest 1000 is [ ].

c. The number 7,369 rounded to the nearest 1,000 is [ ] and to the nearest 10,000 is [ ].

d. The number 73,009 rounded to the nearest 10,000 is [ ] and to the nearest 100,000 is [ ].

PROBLEM SOLVING

At school, Lincoln has been learning all about big numbers. At home, in the privacy of his converted linen closet, he has drawn his own place value grid and added some counters.

1

M	HTh	TTh	Th	H	T	O
Millions	Hundred Thousands	Ten Thousands	Thousands	Hundreds	Tens	Ones

a. What number has he created?

b. He adds 3 counters to the 'Tens' column. What is his new number?

c. He removes the 3 counters from the 'Tens' column and adds them to the 'Hundred Thousands' column. What is his new number?

d. He removes the 3 counters from the 'Hundred Thousands' column and adds them to the 'Ones' column. What is his new number?

2 Lincoln has now written the digits from his place value grid on number cards.

a. Use all the digits to create the highest number possible.

b. Use all the digits to create the lowest number possible.

c. Lincoln makes a new number with the digit cards and gives Clyde some clues to guess what it is. Can you help Clyde work out what Lincoln's number could be? Write down all the possibilities.

> The number has 5 digits. The number is greater than 50,000.
> The number has 9 ones. The number has the same number of tens and thousands.
> The number is less than 80,000. The 1-digit card has not been used.

NEGATIVE NUMBERS

It is winter in Royal Woods and the Loud family are desperate to go sledging. They can only go after school at 4pm and Lisa has worked out that the best conditions for sledging are when the temperature is between -1°C and -4 °C.

1

The - sign on these numbers make them negative numbers.
Negative numbers are numbers that are less than zero.

Which of the days will be best for sledging at 4pm? Complete the table below.

	Temperature at midday	Change in temperature between midday and 4pm	4pm temperature	Best for sledging? ✔ or ✗
Monday	4°C	-8°C	(4 - 8 = -4) -4°C	
Tuesday	7°C	-6°C		
Wednesday	1°C	-3°C		
Thursday	-1°C	-1°C		
Friday	5°C	-8°C		
Saturday	6°C	-5°C		
Sunday	0°C	-5°C		

2

Using your knowledge of negative numbers, compare the number sentences by lling in the missing greater than (>), less than (<) or equal to (=) symbol. The first one has been done for you.

a. 4 – 8 = -4 ⟶ [<] ⟵ 5 – 7= -2

b. -3 + 5 ⟶ [ ] ⟵ -4 + 6

c. -8 + 9 ⟶ [ ] ⟵ -3 + 2

d. 6 – 10 ⟶ [ ] ⟵ 4 – 5

e. 6 – 10 ⟶ [ ] ⟵ -11 + 7

ROMAN NUMERALS

Lucy Loud is obsessed with all things spooky and ancient. While hanging out at the cemetery, she's spotted Roman numerals etched into the oldest gravestones. Each numeral has a different value.

I = 1, V = 5, X = 10, L = 50, C = 100, D = 500 and M = 1000.

These numerals can be joined together to make different values. When a smaller number is in front of a larger number, you subtract it, e.g., IV = 4 and XC = 90.

1

Put a tick next to the correct Roman numeral.

a. 80 =	XC	◯	LXXX	◯	XIV	◯	LXI	◯
b. 501 =	ID	◯	XC	◯	DI	◯	CXXXII	◯
c. 94 =	XCIV	◯	DIV	◯	MII	◯	LXX	◯
d. 990 =	CMXC	◯	MMC	◯	CVii	◯	CLXVI	◯
e. 18 =	VIII	◯	DL	◯	XV	◯	XVIII	◯

2

Fill in this table using numbers and Roman numerals.

a.	134	=		e.		=	DLXXI
b.	804	=		f.		=	XXIX
c.		=	DCCLXX	g.	554	=	
d.		=	CCCLXII	h.	880	=	

3

Put these years in order from earliest to latest.

MMXXII	MDCC	MCCLVI	MDCCCV	MCDXLI

ADDITION

Lynn has had a fun week competing in the Royal Woods Sporting Championships. She's recorded her scores for each day and wants to work out which day she had the highest total.

The best way for Lynn to work out her highest score is to add the two numbers together using the column method. When using this method, you start with the ones column and work to the left to the tens, hundreds then thousands column. When you add more than nine in one column, you 'carry' over the first digit to the column on its left.

If, one day, Lynn received a score of 2178 in kickboxing and 1356 in Mexican wrestling, her overall score is 3534.

	Th	H	T	O
	2	1	7	8
+	1	3	5	6
	3	5	3	4
			1	1

1 Help Lynn work out her scores for each day.

a. Monday
```
    3 5 7 6
  + 2 3 1 2
  _____
```

b. Tuesday
```
    7 3 8 4
  + 1 2 8 4
  _____
```

c. Wednesday
```
    3 9 1 4
  +   3 0 8
  _____
```

d. Thursday
```
    4 5 6 7
  + 3 4 5 6
  _____
```

e. Friday
```
    7 7 6 2
  + 1 0 2 8
  _____
```

f. Saturday
```
    5 0 6 7
  +   7 6 4
  _____
```

g. Sunday
```
    5 3 4 5
  + 3 2 7 7
  _____
```

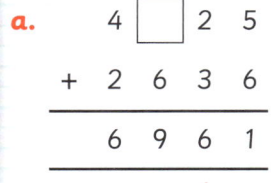

2 Uh oh, Lynn has accidentally spilt her cookie dough milkshake all over her score sheets!

Can you help her work out the missing numbers?

a.
```
    4 ☐ 2 5
  + 2 6 3 6
  _____
    6 9 6 1
          1
```

b.
```
    5 1 2 1
  + 2 ☐ 8 3
  _____
    7 3 0 ☐
        1
```

c.
```
    4 4 5 8
  + 3 5 ☐ 8
  _____
    ☐ 0 4 6
    1 1 1
```

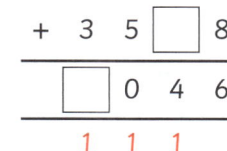

SUBTRACTION

Lori Loud is literally glued to her mobile phone, it is her most valuable possession! She is constantly checking how much memory she has left on her phone, to make sure she will never miss a message from her beloved boyfriend Bobby.

Her phone memory is 9134mb and she notices that messages from Bobby are taking up 1356mb of her phone's memory. How much memory has she got left? To work this out, Lori can use the column method.

Remember, when you carry out subtraction with big numbers, you always start with the ones column and work to the left. If you do not have enough to subtract from in the ones column, you can 'borrow' from the tens column. If you do not have enough in the tens column, you can 'borrow' from the hundreds column, and so on. **9134 - 1356 = ?**

```
  Th   H    T    O
  ⁸9  ¹⁰1  ¹²3   ¹4
-  1   3    5    6
_____
   7   7    7    8
```

Lori has worked out she has 7778mb of memory left. Phew!

1

Use the column method to work out the answers to these subtraction questions.

a.
```
  8 7 5 4
- 2 3 1 1
_____
```

b.
```
  6 5 3 9
- 3 4 2 8
_____
```

c.
```
  5 6 3 2
-   7 6 3
_____
```

d.
```
  9 6 3 8
- 6 3 2 1
_____
```

e.
```
  7 9 4 4
- 6 4 3 8
_____
```

f.
```
  8 5 3 3
- 3 1 7 6
_____
```

2

Bobby has helped Lori work out some of these questions. They have been comparing their answers and realised they don't match! Which of the two has worked out the subtraction correctly? Circle the correct calculation for each question.

Lori	Bobby

a.
Lori:
```
  ⁵6 ¹¹2 ¹1 5
-  3  8  3 3
_____
   2  3  8 2
```
Bobby:
```
  6 2/ ¹1 5
- 3 8  3  3
_____
  3 9  8  2
```

b.
Lori:
```
  7 5 ³4 ¹4
- 2 4  1  9
_____
  5 1  2  5
```
Bobby:
```
  7 5 4 4¹
- 2 4 1 9
_____
  5 1 3 5
```

c.
Lori:
```
  ¹2 6 ¹4 8
-     8 2 9
_____
  1   8 2 1
```
Bobby:
```
  2/ 6/ 4/ 8
-      8 2 9
_____
   1   8 1 9
```

8

MENTAL ADDITION AND SUBTRACTION

Lisa is helping Luna and Luan with their maths. She's written statements about numbers and stuck them around the Loud house. Can you work out whether the statements are true or false?

1
Write **true** or **false** under each statement.

a. When an even number is added to an even number, the answer is always even.

b. When an odd number is added to an odd number, the answer is always odd.

c. When an odd number is added to an odd number, the answer is always even.

d. When you count forwards in 10s from 100, you will say the number 9800.

e. When you count backwards in 25s from 1000, you will say the number 175.

2

Lincoln has been working out how much more money he needs to save to buy a new bike from Biker Gear. The bike he wants costs £110, and he already has £61 saved in his piggy bank. To work out how much he still needs, he draws a simple bar diagram and works it out in his head.

> 110 - 60 is 50, then takeaway one more is 49.

110	
61	**49**

He realises he needs to save another £49.

Help Lincoln to fill in the missing numbers on these bar diagrams.

a.
250	
121	

b.
342	
	132

c.
1559	
	1250

d.
161	
	41

e.
190	534

f.
703	227

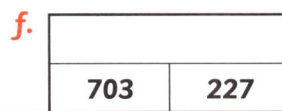

MENTAL ADDITION AND SUBTRACTION

Lana and Lola may be twins but their taste in TV couldn't be more different! Lana loves DIY programmes and Lola loves shows about fashion. When working out what to watch, the sisters try to make it fair.

On Saturday, Lana chose a programme on mechanics for 20 minutes in the morning and 60 minutes in the afternoon. Lola watched a catwalk show for 50 minutes in the morning.

How many more minutes of choice does Lola have in the evening to make it equal with her sister?

Lana		Lola
20 minutes + 60 minutes	=	50 minutes + 30 minutes

Lola is allowed 30 more minutes of choice to make it equal.

1

Using mental strategies, fill in the missing numbers to make these number equations balance.

a. $60 + 30$ = $40 + 50$

b. $110 - 50$ = $30 + \boxed{}$

c. $85 + \boxed{}$ = $120 - 15$

d. $290 + \boxed{}$ = $160 + 245$

e. $165 + 230$ = $500 - \boxed{}$

f. $250 - \boxed{}$ = $-86 + 118$

g. $\boxed{} + 328$ = $-500 - 160$

h. $450 - 230$ = $145 + \boxed{}$

i. $342 - 50$ = $\boxed{} + 150$

j. $20 + \boxed{}$ = $290 - 135$

Look at this number pyramid. The numbers below always add up to the number above.

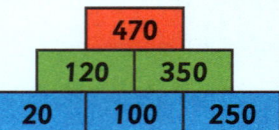

For example:
$20 + 100 = 120$ and $120 - 100 = 20$
$100 + 250 = 350$ and $350 - 100 = 250$
$120 + 350 = 470$ and $470 - 120 = 350$
This is why 470 is at the top of the pyramid.

2

Fill in the missing numbers on the number pyramids below.

a.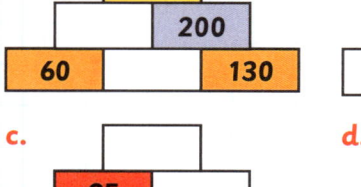

b.

c.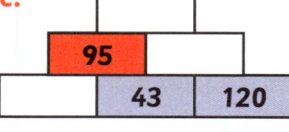

d.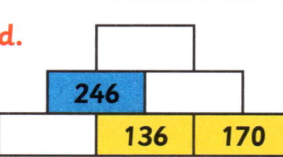

ADDITION AND SUBTRACTION

When solving multistep word problems, there will be more than one calculation that you need to do before finding your answer. Look at how Leni solved this problem below.

Leni is designing her latest hair accessory out of three different types of ribbon. The red ribbon is 129cm long, the yellow ribbon is 150cm long and the pink ribbon is 85cm longer than the yellow.

She needs all the pieces of ribbon to be 120cm long. When she has cut them all to the correct length, how much ribbon will she have left over in total?

Red ribbon: 129 - 120 = 9cm left over.
Yellow ribbon: 150 - 120 = 30cm left over.
Pink ribbon: length (150 + 85) = 235cm. 235 - 120 = 115cm left over.
Total left over = 9 + 30 + 115 = 154cm of ribbon.

1 Luna is shopping for guitars. She has some vouchers that she got for her birthday - £50 from her Mum and Dad and £20 from her siblings — and she's saved £85.20 in her piggy bank. The guitar she wants to buy is £135. Can she afford it? How much money will she have left over?

2 The Loud family are going on a road trip to Aloha Beach. On the first day, they drive 130km. On the second day they drive double that. On the third day, they only drive 37km before they realise the petrol light has come on! They began the journey on a full tank of petrol and normally the car can go 500km before they need to fill up. The next petrol station is 15km away. Will they make it? How many km worth of petrol will they have to spare?

3 Lisa is measuring out the chemicals for her latest science experiment. In beaker **A** she adds 270ml of a red liquid and 323ml of a blue liquid. In beaker **B** she adds 180ml of a yellow liquid and 135ml of a green liquid. What is the difference in the amount of liquids in the two beakers?

4 Bobby Santiago has lots of jobs and works super hard! This week, he has worked a total of 1250 minutes. He worked for 235 minutes delivering pizza, 380 minutes as a lifeguard and 220 minutes as a security guard. He's spent the rest of the time stocking shelves at the supermarket. How many minutes has he worked at the supermarket this week?

PRIME NUMBERS

Luna Loud loves to rock out! Today she's writing a rock song about prime numbers. Can you help her identify the prime numbers so she can use them in her song lyrics?

A prime number is a number that is only divisible by one and itself, e.g., 13.

1 Circle all the guitars that have a prime number between 1 and 50.

2   4   9   11   15   24

29   33   37   45   47   50

2 Write all the prime numbers between the following numbers.

a. **50 – 59:**

b. **60 – 69:**

c. **70 – 79:**

d. **80 – 89:**

e. **90 – 99:**

3 Which two prime numbers between 0 and 20 have been added in each of these sums?

a. ☐ + ☐ = 8   *b.* ☐ + ☐ = 28

c. ☐ + ☐ = 15   *d.* ☐ + ☐ = 21

WRITTEN MULTIPLICATION

Lincoln is crazy about comics. When he visits the Mega Comics shop, he uses multiplication to work out how many of each comic they have.

There are 186 copies of 4 different editions of Ace Savvy.

By multiplying the numbers, he has worked out there are 744 copies in total.

```
  H  T  O
  1  8  6
x        4
_____
  7  4  4
  3  2
```

1

Use your multiplication skills to work out the answers to these questions. Remember to start by multiplying the ones, then the tens and finally the hundreds. If you need to carry a number, write it underneath the next column.

Answer these questions using a written method.

a.
```
  H  T  O
  2  4  6
x        3
_____
_____
```

b.
```
  H  T  O
  1  9  9
x        4
_____
_____
```

c.
```
  H  T  O
  4  0  1
x        2
_____
_____
```

d.
```
  H  T  O
  1  5  0
x        5
_____
_____
```

e.
```
  H  T  O
  3  1  8
x        5
_____
_____
```

f.
```
  H  T  O
  4  0  9
x        7
_____
_____
```

g.
```
  H  T  O
  7  1  5
x        6
_____
_____
```

h.
```
  H  T  O
  3  6  7
x        8
_____
_____
```

2

Match the question to the correct answer. Use this space for your workings out.

a. 465 x 3 =   2055

b. 411 x 5 =   5496

c. 362 x 4 =   1395

d. 916 x 6 =   1448

WRITTEN MULTIPLICATION

Lincoln wants to work out how many David's Castle comics Mega Comics has in stock. To work this out, he's counted that there are 48 copies of 23 different editions.

When multiplying a two-digit number by another two-digit number, you might wish to use the grid method. Fill in the missing numbers in the boxes and work out the answer by adding the numbers together. For example:

48 x 23 =

x	40	8	
20	800	160	960
3	120	24	+144
			1104

There are 1104 copies of David's Castle comics in store.

1

Complete these multiplication questions using the same method.

a.

24 x 19 =

x	20	4
10		
9		

_____

b.

35 x 43 =

x	30	5
40		
3		

_____

c.

36 x 25 =

x	30	6
20		
5		

_____

d.

66 x 33 =

x	60	6
30		
3		

_____

Another way to work out multiplication questions is to use the column method. Remember to put a 0 down when you multiply the tens. E.g.

```
        4 3
      x 2 3
43 x 3 = 1 2 9
43 x 20 = 8 6 0
        9 8 9
```

2

Use the column method to work out the answers to these questions.

a.
```
    3 4
  x 2 1
  _____
```

b.
```
    2 3
  x 2 2
  _____
```

c.
```
    3 4
  x 1 9
  _____
```

WRITTEN DIVISION

Lynn Sr. is doing a stock take at his restaurant, Lynn's Table. He needs 6 mushrooms per portion to make his liso soup and he has 453 mushrooms in the fridge. Lynn Sr. uses the formal written method of division to work out how many portions of soup he can make.

When doing written division, you always begin on the left. For each column, if there are any remainders, they are 'carried over' to the next column.

453 ÷ 6 is written as

$$6 \,\big|\, \begin{array}{ccc} 0 & 7 & 5 \\ 4 & {}_4 5 & {}_3 3 \end{array} \; r3$$

With 453 mushrooms in the fridge, Lynn Sr. can make 75 portions of 'Liso Soup' with 3 mushrooms left over.

- 6 doesn't go into 4.
- 6 into 45 goes 7 times with a remainder of 3 (this 3 is carried over to the next column).
- 6 into 33 goes 5 times with a remainder of 3.

1

Use the written method to work out the answer to these questions.

a.
6 | 8 5 2

b.
7 | 5 4 3

c.
8 | 5 6 7

d.
9 | 9 6 7

2

Can you do the same for these longer numbers?

a.
4 | 5 2 0 9

b.
8 | 4 0 3 5

c.
3 | 8 0 1 6

d.
7 | 2 3 3 7

3

Use your division knowledge to work out the missing numbers in these questions.

a.
7 ☐ 1 r2
3 | 2 3 7 5

b.
7 4 2 r2
☐ | 3 7 1 2

c.
4 2 5
6 | 2 5 ☐ 0

d.
6 2 4 ☐
9 | 5 6 2 4

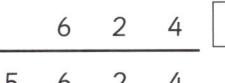

WRITTEN DIVISION

Some of the ingredients at Lynn's Table come in big packs, so Lynn Sr. has to do some tricky maths to work out how to divide them.

The croutons for Lynn Sr.'s Lu-Caesar salad come in a pack of 1742 and he needs 13 croutons per portion. There are lots of different ways to work out how many portions of salad he can make with one bag of croutons. Here's one example of how to do it.

$1742 \div 13 =$

```
        0  1  3  4
13 |  1  7  4  2
      1  3  ↓  ↓
         4  4
         3  9
            5  2
            5  2
               0
```

- 13 goes into 17 once (13) with 4 remaining.
- The 4 is written underneath and the 4 in the next column is brought down to make 44.
- 13 into 44 goes 3 times (39) with 5 left over.
- The 5 is written underneath and the 2 in the next column is brought down to make 52.
- 13 into 52 goes 4 times with no remainders.

1 Work out the answers to these long division questions.
The 12 times table has been shown to help you with the working out.

a.

```
12 |  1  4  7  6
```

b.

```
12 |  1  7  4  0
```

c.

```
12 |  1  8  6  0
```

d.

```
12 |  3  7  4  4
```

1 x 12 =	12
2 x 12 =	24
3 x 12 =	36
4 x 12 =	48
5 x 12 =	60
6 x 12 =	72
7 x 12 =	84
8 x 12 =	96
9 x 12 =	108
10 x 12 =	120
11 x 12 =	132
12 x 12 =	144

FRACTIONS

The Loud family like nothing better than getting a delivery of pizzas! With lots of mouths to feed, it is important that enough pizzas are ordered for the family and they are shared equally.

 The fraction of pizzas covered in cheese can be written as:

$2\frac{1}{4}$ (mixed number fraction) or $\frac{9}{4}$ (improper fraction)

1 Fill in the table, writing the fraction of pizza covered in cheese as an improper fraction and mixed number fraction.

b. $\frac{1}{4}$ of 16 = ☐

Mixed number fraction	Improper fraction

2 Write these mixed number fractions as improper fractions e.g. $2\frac{3}{5} = \frac{13}{5}$

a. $3\frac{2}{3} = \frac{☐}{☐}$

b. $2\frac{4}{7} = \frac{☐}{☐}$

c. $6\frac{1}{2} = \frac{☐}{☐}$

d. $5\frac{2}{5} = \frac{☐}{☐}$

e. $4\frac{1}{6} = \frac{☐}{☐}$

f. $7\frac{3}{4} = \frac{☐}{☐}$

3 Convert these improper fractions to mixed number fractions.

a. $\frac{8}{3} = ☐\frac{☐}{☐}$

b. $\frac{17}{6} = ☐\frac{☐}{☐}$

c. $\frac{17}{5} = ☐\frac{☐}{☐}$

d. $\frac{19}{2} = ☐\frac{☐}{☐}$

e. $\frac{21}{4} = ☐\frac{☐}{☐}$

f. $\frac{22}{7} = ☐\frac{☐}{☐}$

ADDING FRACTIONS

Lola dedicates a lot of her time to taking part in (and winning!) beauty pageants. Scores are always given in fractions and she's checking her score cards to see what her score adds up to.

When adding fractions, Lola knows that if the denominator (the bottom number) of the two fractions are the same then you simply add the numerators (top numbers) together: $\frac{1}{5} + \frac{3}{5} = \frac{4}{5}$

1 Add these fractions together and write each answer as an improper fraction.

a. $\frac{2}{6} + \frac{5}{6} = \frac{\square}{\square}$

b. $\frac{13}{10} + \frac{6}{10} = \frac{\square}{\square}$

c. $\frac{3}{4} + \frac{3}{4} + \frac{1}{4} = \frac{\square}{\square}$

d. $\frac{19}{8} + \frac{5}{8} + \frac{13}{8} = \frac{\square}{\square}$

2 When the denominator is different you need to find a common multiple and make an equivalent fraction e.g. $\frac{3}{4} + \frac{2}{3}$ has a common denominator of 12 so $\frac{9}{12} + \frac{8}{12} = \frac{17}{12}$

Find a common denominator and work out these fraction sums.
Write your answers as improper fractions.

a. $\frac{1}{2} + \frac{2}{6} = \frac{\square}{\square}$

b. $\frac{3}{5} + \frac{7}{10} = \frac{\square}{\square}$

c. $\frac{1}{4} + \frac{1}{3} = \frac{\square}{\square}$

d. $\frac{1}{2} + \frac{4}{5} = \frac{\square}{\square}$

e. $\frac{3}{4} + \frac{3}{5} = \frac{\square}{\square}$

f. $\frac{2}{3} + \frac{3}{5} = \frac{\square}{\square}$

3 Complete the fraction sums and draw a circle around all the answers that would be 3 or more as a mixed number fraction.

a. $\frac{5}{3} + \frac{7}{6} = \boxed{}$

b. $\frac{5}{2} + \frac{4}{3} = \boxed{}$

c. $\frac{9}{5} + \frac{12}{10} = \boxed{}$

d. $\frac{7}{5} + \frac{14}{10} = \boxed{}$

e. $\frac{10}{4} + \frac{10}{5} = \boxed{}$

f. $\frac{7}{3} + \frac{4}{5} = \boxed{}$

SUBTRACTING FRACTIONS

When Lola is at a beauty pageant, she's sometimes given a score she doesn't agree with! Lola likes to scrub these ones from her memory and take them off her final score.

When subtracting fractions where the denominator (the bottom number) of the two fractions is the same, you simply subtract one numerator (top number) from the other numerator. For example: $\frac{3}{5} - \frac{1}{5} = \frac{2}{5}$

1 Solve these subtraction questions and write your answers as improper fractions.

a. $\frac{17}{8} - \frac{4}{8} = \dfrac{\square}{\square}$

b. $\frac{9}{2} - \frac{4}{2} = \dfrac{\square}{\square}$

c. $\frac{13}{4} - \frac{5}{4} = \dfrac{\square}{\square}$

d. $\frac{13}{3} - \frac{5}{3} = \dfrac{\square}{\square}$

2 When the denominator is different, you need to find a common multiple and make an equivalent fraction e.g. $\frac{3}{4} - \frac{2}{3}$ has a common denominator of 12 so $\frac{9}{12} - \frac{8}{12} = \frac{1}{12}$.

Work out the answers to these subtraction questions and write your answers as improper fractions.

a. $\frac{8}{2} - \frac{5}{6} = \boxed{}$

b. $\frac{10}{4} - \frac{7}{5} = \boxed{}$

c. $\frac{14}{5} - \frac{4}{3} = \boxed{}$

d. $\frac{6}{2} - \frac{9}{5} = \boxed{}$

3 Complete these number sentences and then choose the correct sign <,> or = to fill the box. The first one has been done for you.

a. $\frac{9}{2} - \frac{3}{2} = \frac{18}{10} - \frac{15}{10} = \frac{3}{10} < 1$

b. $\frac{24}{3} - \frac{9}{2} = \dfrac{\square}{\square} - \dfrac{\square}{\square} = \dfrac{\square}{\square} \ \boxed{} \ 3$

c. $\frac{9}{2} - \frac{6}{3} = \dfrac{\square}{\square} - \dfrac{\square}{\square} = \dfrac{\square}{\square} \ \boxed{} \ 1$

d. $\frac{8}{2} - \frac{12}{5} = \dfrac{\square}{\square} - \dfrac{\square}{\square} = \dfrac{\square}{\square} \ \boxed{} \ 2$

e. $\frac{7}{3} - \frac{2}{4} = \dfrac{\square}{\square} - \dfrac{\square}{\square} = \dfrac{\square}{\square} \ \boxed{} \ 1$

f. $\frac{7}{3} - \frac{1}{5} = \dfrac{\square}{\square} - \dfrac{\square}{\square} = \dfrac{\square}{\square} \ \boxed{} \ 2$

MULTIPLYING FRACTIONS

According to brainbox Lisa, multiplying fractions is easy!
You simply need to multiply the numerator by the numerator and multiply the denominator by the denominator.

For example:
$\frac{3}{5}$ x $\frac{1}{3}$ = (3 x 1 = 3) and (5 x 3 = 15)
therefore the answer is $\frac{3}{15}$
You can then simplify the fraction:
$\frac{3}{15}$ = $\frac{1}{5}$

At the pizzeria where Bobby works, they sell pizza slices as a mix and match. Sometimes people come in with the trickiest orders! Today, someone wants to order $\frac{2}{5}$ ham and pineapple $\frac{2}{5}$ mushroom and $\frac{2}{5}$ pepperoni. Bobby needs to know exactly how much pizza he needs to make for this order.

What is $\frac{2}{5}$ x3?

Steps to multiplying a fraction by a whole number:
- Turn the whole number into a fraction by making the denominator 1. E.g. 3 = $\frac{3}{1}$
- Multiply the numerators together: 2 x 3 = 6
- Multiply the denominators together: 5 x 1 = 5
- This will give an improper fraction: $\frac{6}{5}$
- Convert the improper fraction into a proper (vulgar) fraction $\frac{6}{5}$ = $1\frac{1}{5}$

This means Bobby will need to make 1 whole pizza and $\frac{1}{5}$ of a pizza for this order.

1

Match the multiplying fraction number sentences with its answer in the simplest form.

a. $\frac{1}{4}$ x $\frac{2}{3}$ $\frac{1}{5}$

b. $\frac{3}{5}$ x $\frac{1}{3}$ $\frac{2}{27}$

c. $\frac{4}{8}$ x $\frac{2}{4}$ $\frac{1}{6}$

d. $\frac{6}{7}$ x $\frac{3}{5}$ $\frac{18}{35}$

e. $\frac{1}{6}$ x $\frac{4}{9}$ $\frac{1}{4}$

2

Fill in the missing boxes to work out how much pizza he will need to make for the following orders:

Pizza order		Calculation	How many pizzas will he need to make?
	$\frac{1}{2}$ cheese $\frac{1}{2}$ mushroom	$\frac{1}{2}$ x2	
	$\frac{4}{6}$ vegetables $\frac{4}{6}$ pepperoni $\frac{4}{6}$ cheese	$\frac{4}{6}$ x3	
	$\frac{3}{8}$ pineapple $\frac{3}{8}$ ham $\frac{3}{8}$ pepper $\frac{3}{8}$ meatballs		

ORDERING FRACTIONS

Lisa is doing her favourite thing, playing teacher, by giving her sisters a quick recap on fractions and decimals.

- A decimal is a number that is in between whole numbers and written with a dot.
- A proper fraction is a fraction that is less than one.
- An improper fraction is fraction that is greater than one.
- A mixed fraction is an improper fraction that is written as a sum of a whole number and a fraction.

1 Can you help the Loud girls rewrite these fractions and decimals in order from smallest to greatest?

a. $\frac{1}{4}$ $\frac{3}{4}$ 0.5 $\frac{1}{8}$ 0.8 $\frac{7}{10}$

b. $\frac{10}{12}$ $\frac{1}{9}$ 0.1 $\frac{5}{10}$ $\frac{1}{3}$ $\frac{2}{8}$

c. $1\frac{1}{4}$ 0.4   0.7 $\frac{10}{5}$ $2\frac{2}{3}$ $\frac{1}{2}$

d. $1\frac{3}{4}$ $\frac{7}{2}$ 0.25 $\frac{1}{8}$ 0.3 $\frac{9}{6}$

2 Now colour the boxes where you have written the fractions and decimals according to the key below:

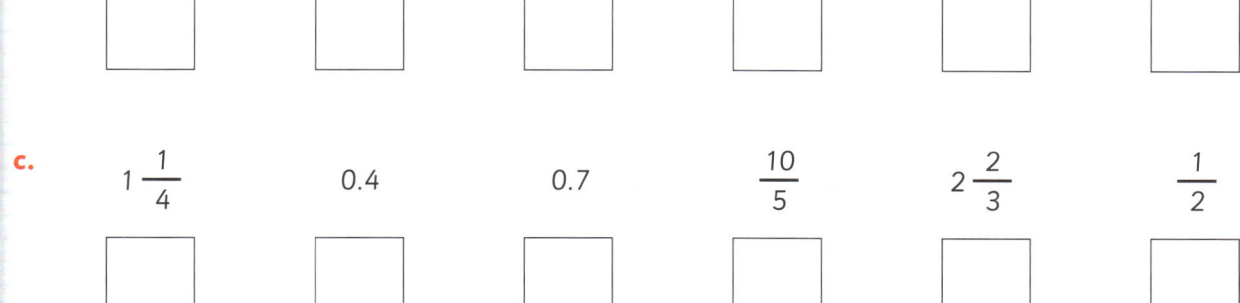

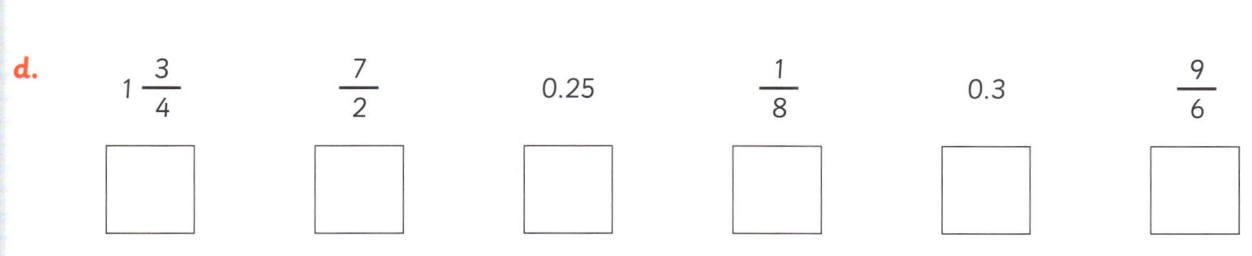

Improper fractions: colour in **red**

Proper fractions: colour in **blue**

Mixed fractions: colour in **green**

Decimals: colour in **yellow**

RATIO AND PROPORTION

Lola is obsessed with perfume. She has a VERY important beauty pageant coming up so has been experimenting with mixing different liquids to find the perfect scented perfume to win over the judges.

She has mixed 4 green tubes and 8 yellow tubes for perfume 1. The proportion of green tubes is 4 out of 12. The ratio of green to yellow tubes is 4:8 simplified as 1:2.

1

Complete these:

a.

Proportion of blue tubes is

___ out of ___.

The ratio of blue to green

tubes is ___:___

simplified as ___:___.

b.

Proportion of blue tubes is

___ out of ___.

The ratio of blue to purple

tubes is ___:___.

c.

Proportion of purple tubes is

____ out of ____.

The ratio of purple to green

tubes is ___:___

simplified as ___:___.

2

 Lola's favourite perfume mixture has the ratio of 3 purple tubes to 5 green tubes.

After her success, Lola has decided to make the perfect scents for some of her sisters too. These are the ratios they like best. Colour in the following to make their perfect perfumes:

a. Luna: 4 green to 1 red (4:1)

b. Leni: 2 red to 5 purple (2:5)

c. Lori: 4 brown to 6 red (4:6)

PERCENTAGES

Leni is shopping at the mall. Her favourite shop has a sale on so Leni needs to understand percentages to work out how much money she will save.

'Per cent' (%) means 'out of 100'. It is a whole that has been divided into 100 parts so, for example, 60% means 60 out of 100.

1

Help Leni to find the percentages of these numbers.

a. 50% of 100 = ☐   **g.** 50% of 200 = ☐

b. 25% of 100 = ☐   **h.** 25% of 200 = ☐

c. 10% of 100 = ☐   **i.** 10% of 200 = ☐

d. 5% of 100 = ☐   **j.** 5% of 200 = ☐

e. 30% of 100 = ☐   **k.** 30% of 200 = ☐

f. 70% of 100 = ☐   **l.** 70% of 200 = ☐

2

Leni has spotted a dress with a price tag of £25 that has 10% off. To work out the new price of the dress, Leni first needs to work out 10% of £25: 25 ÷ 10 = 2.5, so 10% of £25 is £2.50.

Next, Leni needs to subtract the 10% saving from the original price of the dress: 25 - 2.50 = 22.50 so the new price of the dress is £22.50. What a bargain!

Draw lines to match each clothing label with the correct saving and new price. The first one has been done for you.

Clothes label	Saving	New price
£25 10% OFF	£7.50 off	£48.00
£60 20% OFF	£2.50 off	£70.00
£50 15% OFF	£4.25 off	£42.50
£85 5% OFF	£12.00 off	£22.50
£100 30% OFF	£30.00 off	£80.75

SCALE FACTORS

Lisa has been working away in her lab on a secret new project – creating an Increasing Machine. Using complicated scientific equations, she's worked out how to increase the size of 2D objects.

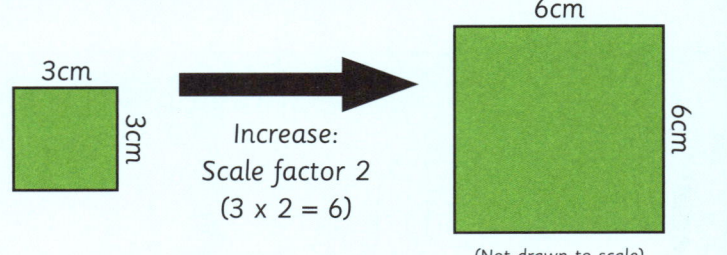

The size by which she chooses to increase these objects is called the scale factor. She tests her machine with a simple 3cm x 3cm square. She programmed the machine to increase its size by the scale factor of 2. This means that the measurements of each side are doubled (x 2).

3cm
3cm
Increase:
Scale factor 2
(3 x 2 = 6)
6cm
6cm
(Not drawn to scale)

1

Here are some more shapes that Lisa has increased in her Increasing Machine. Can you work out the scale factor she used for each of the enlargements? Also fill in the missing lengths.

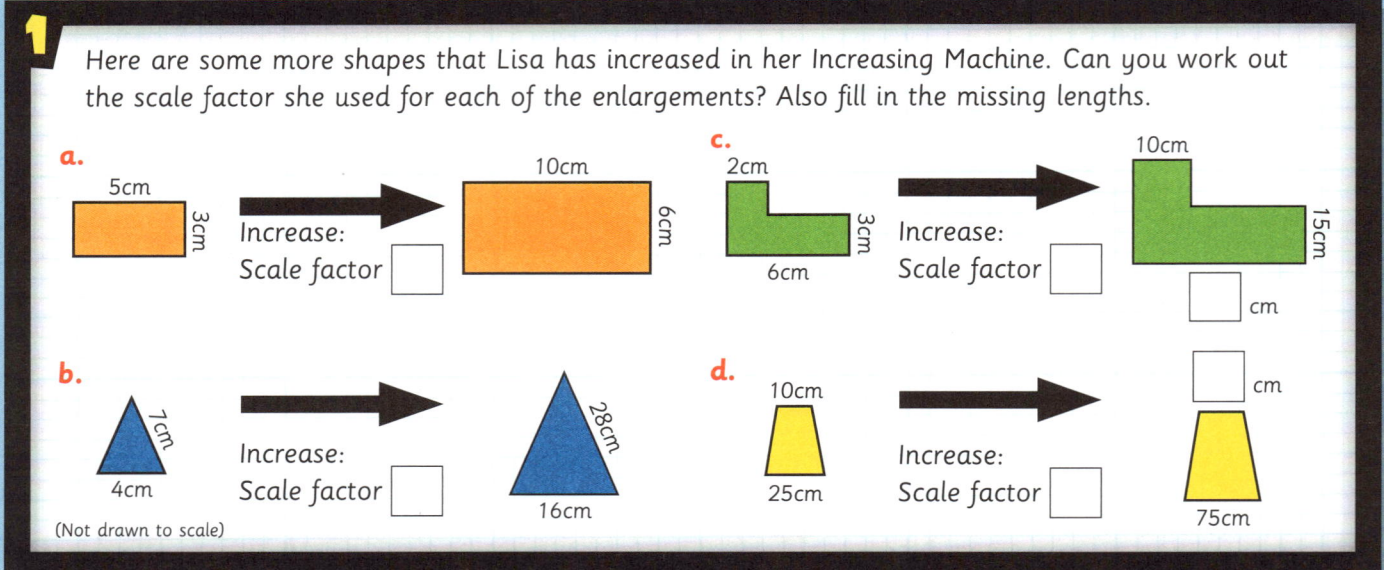

a.
5cm
3cm
Increase: Scale factor ☐
10cm
6cm

b.
7cm
4cm
Increase: Scale factor ☐
28cm
16cm
(Not drawn to scale)

c.
2cm
6cm
3cm
Increase: Scale factor ☐
10cm
15cm
☐ cm

d.
10cm
25cm
Increase: Scale factor ☐
☐ cm
75cm

2

Increase this triangle by the scale factor of 2. Draw the increased shape next to it.
Scale: 1 square = 1cm.

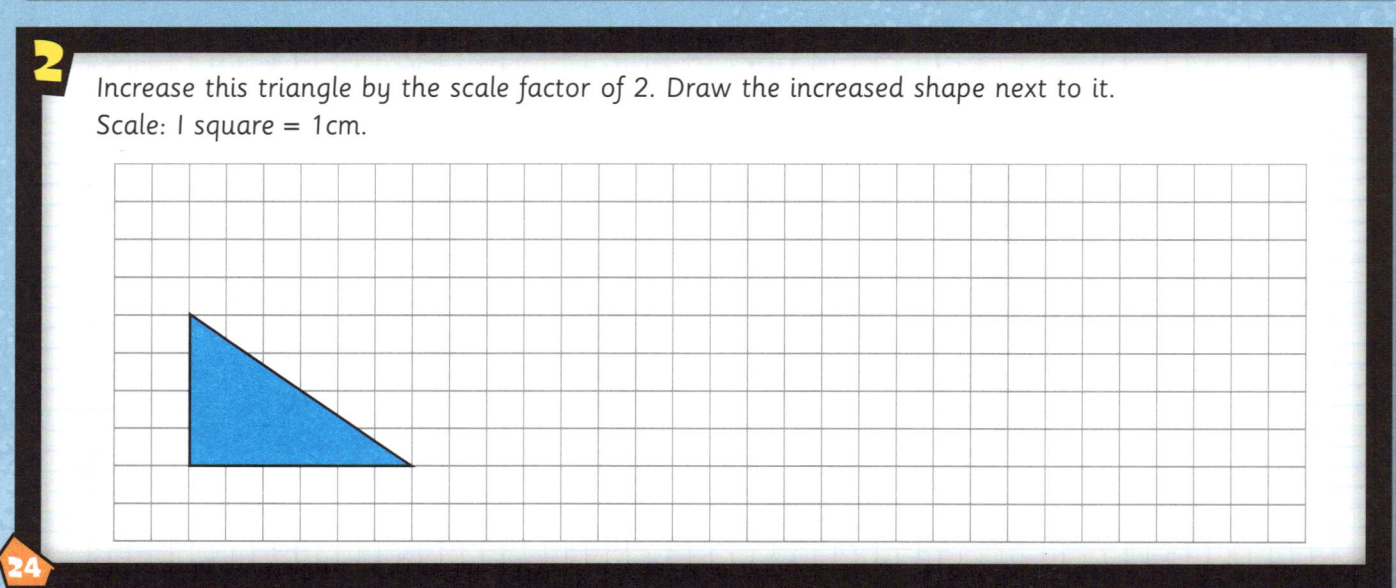

SIMPLE FORMULAE

The Loud house is so loud that Lincoln can't concentrate on his algebra homework. He's retreated to Lisa's bunker in the garden for some peace and quiet.

1

Can you help Lincoln work out the value of the letters? The first one has been done for you.

a. $x + 5 = 9$

$x = \boxed{4}$

b. $y + 7 = 22$

$y = \boxed{}$

c. $n - 6 = 9$

$n = \boxed{}$

d. $x - 7 = 3$

$x = \boxed{}$

e. $7y = 35$

$y = \boxed{}$

f. $\dfrac{x}{6} = 6$

$x = \boxed{}$

2

Now try these trickier sums. The first one has been done for you.

a. $3x + 4 = 10$

$3x = \boxed{6}$

$x = \boxed{2}$

b. $6a + 5 = 29$

$6a = \boxed{}$

$a = \boxed{}$

c. $3n - 2 = 25$

$3n = \boxed{}$

$n = \boxed{}$

d. $2 + 8c = 26$

$8c = \boxed{}$

$c = \boxed{}$

e. $\dfrac{n}{9} + 4 = 9$

$\dfrac{n}{9} = \boxed{}$

$n = \boxed{}$

f. $12 - x = 2$

$x = \boxed{}$

g. $7c + 12 = 47$

$7c = \boxed{}$

$c = \boxed{}$

h. $9 + 6a = 57$

$6a = \boxed{}$

$a = \boxed{}$

i. $43 - 4n = 23$

$4n = \boxed{}$

$n = \boxed{}$

NUMBER SEQUENCES

Lynn is creating a tough training programme that gets harder every day. Can you work out how many times she needs to repeat each exercise each day by using the rule to complete the sequence?

1

Rule	Monday	Tuesday	Wednesday	Thursday	Friday	Saturday	Sunday
Squats (add 6)	2						
Jog (double)	1 minute						
Rest (subtract 7)	42 minutes						
Press-ups (double and add 1)	2						
Jumping jacks (multiply by 3 then add 2)	2						
Box punches (add 4 and double)	2						
Rest (halve and subtract 5)	10 minutes 30 seconds (Tip: convert this to seconds first = 630 seconds)						

ALGEBRA WORD PROBLEMS

The Loud family has some tricky calculations to solve. Use your algebra skills to help them work out the answers.

1

Lana and Lola are trying to work out how many days it is until their next birthday. They know that it is 8 weeks and then 3 more days.

a. Can you write a formula to calculate the number of days until their birthday, where the letter d stands for 'days until birthday' and the letter w stands for 'number of weeks'?

b. Use the formula to work out the number of days until their birthday.

2

Leni is trying to work out whether she has enough pocket money to buy some shiny sequin badges and stars to decorate her new jacket. Sequin badges cost 12p. Stars cost 25p.

a. Write an equation to work out the total cost, using b for sequin badges, s for stars and c for the total cost.

b. She has 75p. Can she afford two sequin badges and two stars?

c. Bobby gives her another 45p. How much does she have altogether now?

d. If she buys three stars, how many sequin badges can she afford?

3

Luna is giving a rock show performance to raise money for a new guitar amp. She wants to make £18.20.

a. Write a formula that calculates how much she needs to charge for each ticket in pence (t) if p is the number of people who buy a ticket, in order to raise the total amount.

b. She thinks that 13 people will pay for tickets. How much should she charge in pounds and pence?

4

Lincoln gave half his Ace Savvy collector cards to Clyde, then bought 3 more packs with his pocket money. Now he has 12 packs. Write a formula to calculate the number of packs that he started with (p) and solve the equation.

CONVERTING UNITS OF MEASUREMENT

Despite their differences, Lana and Lola usually get on well together but for some reason, they are disagreeing about absolutely everything today. Use this conversion table to help you work out who is right.

Capacity	Mass	Length
1 litre (l) = 1000 millilitres (ml)	1 kilogram (kg) = 1000 grams (g)	1 centimetre (cm) = 10 millimetres (mm)
1 centilitre (cl) = 10ml	1 tonne = 1000kg	1 metre (m) = 100cm
		1 kilometre (km) = 1000m

1

Lana says: I have a string that is 5.6m and another that is 650mm. I have the most string.

Lola says: But I have 6 whole metres of string: I have more.

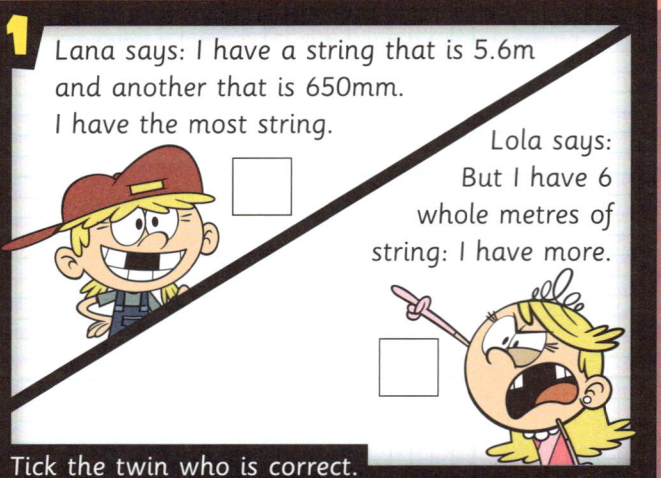

Tick the twin who is correct.

2

Lana says: It is 4.6km drive to the supermarket and then a 250m walk. It is the nearest shop, we should go there!

Lola says: The mall is much nearer, it is just 3.2km and a 535m walk.

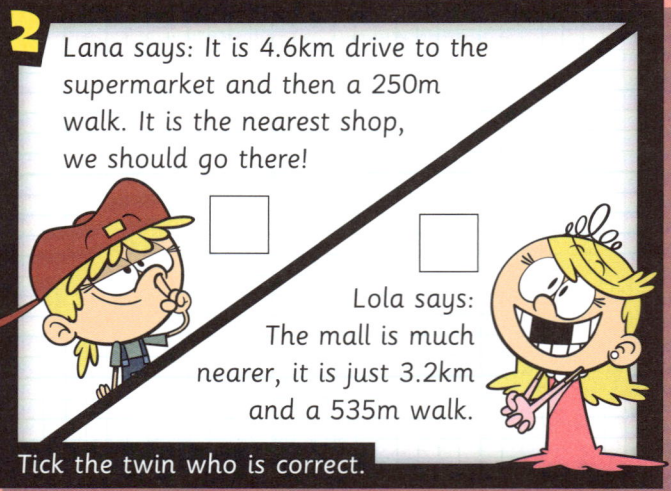

Tick the twin who is correct.

3

Lana says: This bottle of pop is the best value it has 5325ml.

Lola says: No, these cans are better, you get 0.25l in each can and there are 30 cans for the same price.

Tick the twin who is correct.

4

Lana says: This bag of crisps is best, it's huge and weighs half a kg.

Lola says: No, buy this multipack, there are 6 bags of 80g for the same price.

Tick the twin who is correct.

5

Circle the values that are equivalent in each row.

a	35cm	350cl	350mm	3.5cm	3.5m	0.35m
b	0.4kg	400g	40g	400ml	4kg	4g
c	14cl	1.4kg	140g	140ml	0.14l	0.014l
d	1560kg	1560g	15.6 tonnes	1.56 tonnes	15600g	1560000g

PERIMETER

Lincoln and Clyde are helping their neighbours build new garden fences. They have to calculate the gardens' perimeters to work out how many fence panels they need.

Perimeter is the distance around the edges of the shape.

In the example this is 7cm + 3cm + 7cm + 3cm = 20cm

1 Calculate the perimeters for these gardens. 1 square = 1m.

a.

b.

c.

d.

e.

f.

g.

h.

i.

CALCULATING AREA

Lana is helping her neighbours grow grass in their gardens. She needs to work out the area of each garden so she can buy the right amount of grass seed.

1 Look at the gardens on the previous page and calculate the area for each garden.

Remember that area is calculated as square units, in this case square metres or m². Split the gardens into rectangle shapes and then calculate the area of each part by multiplying the width by the length.

a.	b.	c.
d.	e.	f.
g.	h.	i.

2 In the Loud's garden, Luna and Luan are planning on building a den to rival Lisa's bunker. Look at the plan and calculate the area of the different objects in square metres.

Hint: Remember, to work out the area of a triangle, you multiply the height by the width (also known as the base), then divide by 2.

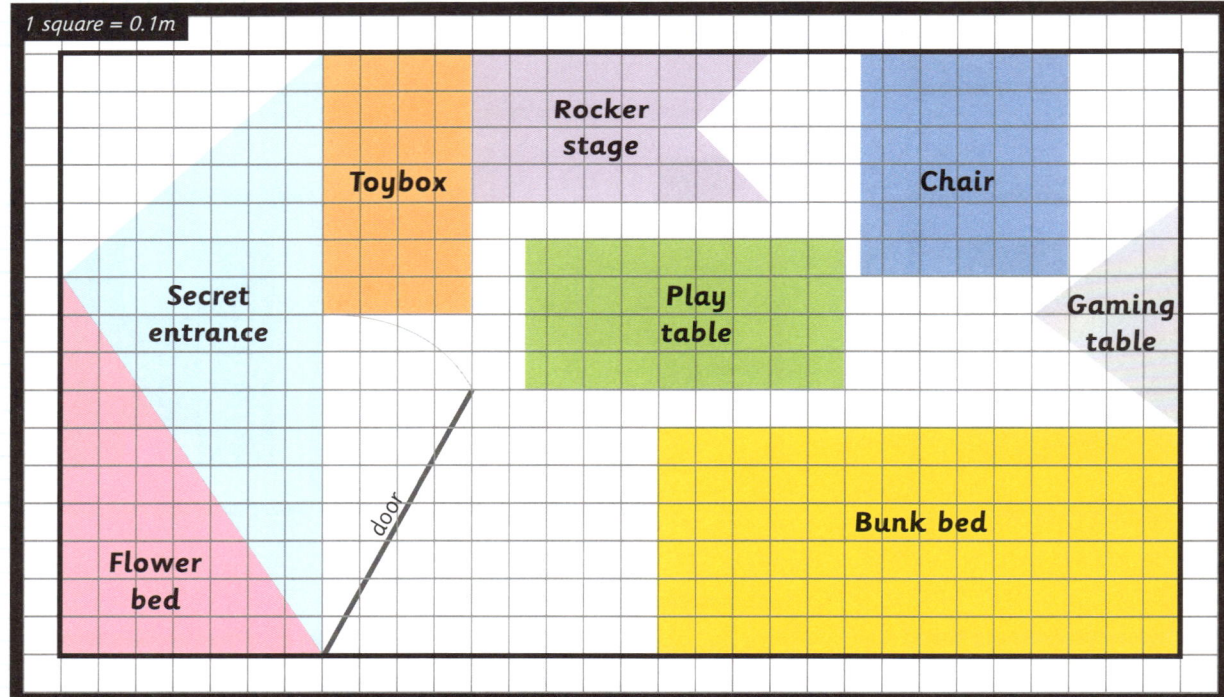

1 square = 0.1m

a. **Bunk bed =**

b. **Gaming table =**

c. **Toybox =**

d. **Secret entrance =**

e. **Play table =**

f. **Flower bed =**

g. **Chair =**

h. **Rocker stage =**

CALCULATING AREA

Lincoln and Lynn are seeing how fast they can skateboard around the two car parks at Royal Woods Middle School. Although the rectangular car parks are different lengths and widths, they both have a perimeter of 72m.

1 Work out how many possible widths and lengths the areas could be, if both have widths and lengths in whole numbers of metres.

2 Can you write a rule that applies to working out any perimeter?

3 Lisa tells Leni that although the two car parks have the same perimeter, they have different areas.

a. What is the width and length that would make the maximum possible area?

b. What is the maximum possible area?

4 Leni says that the two parking areas have a difference of 57m^2.

Work out the possible widths and lengths of the parking areas.

Hint: Use what you know about the possible lengths and widths to work out all of the possible areas until you find two that have a difference in area of 57m^2.

MILES AND KILOMETRES

Lincoln and Clyde have been for a ride on their bikes in Tall Timbers Park. They have worked out the distances they travelled using the maps on their phones.

They realise 1 mile = 1.6km.

1 Work out these distances in km.

Miles	1	5	4.5	9	12.5
Km					

2 Work out these distances in miles.

Miles					
Km	11.2	10.4	9.6	16	5.6

3 Who has travelled furthest? Use the <, > and = signs to complete these number sentences.

Lincoln	<, > or =	Clyde
3 miles		4km
3.5 miles		5.6km
5.5 miles		8km
8 miles		13km
11.5 miles		18.4km

ANGLES

The Loud family are at Hole in One-derland crazy golf. Lisa is determined to win so, she's using her knowledge of angles to make sure she gets a hole in one every time.

When two points meet at a shared point, it creates an angle. The bigger the space between the two lines, the bigger the angle. The size of an angle is measures in degrees (°).
There are four types of angles that you need to remember:

Right angle	Acute angle	Obtuse angle	Reflex angle
A right angle is exactly 90°. A square is made up of 4 right angles.	An acute angle is any angle which is smaller than 90°.	An obtuse angle is any angle between 90° and 180°.	A reflex angle is any angle between 180° and 360°.

1 Look at the different angles below. Underneath each one, write down whether it is a right, acute, obtuse or reflex angle.

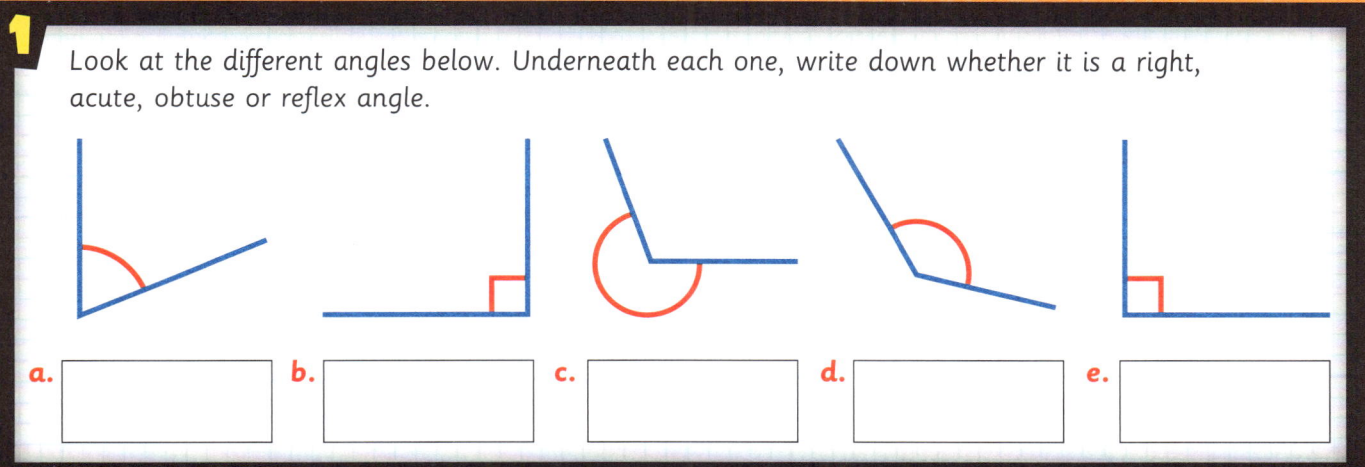

a.

b.

c.

d.

e.

2 Look at the marked angles on the shapes below. Use the colour key to shade the angles the correct colour.

Obtuse 🟨   **Acute** 🟩   **Right** 🟥   **Reflex** 🟦

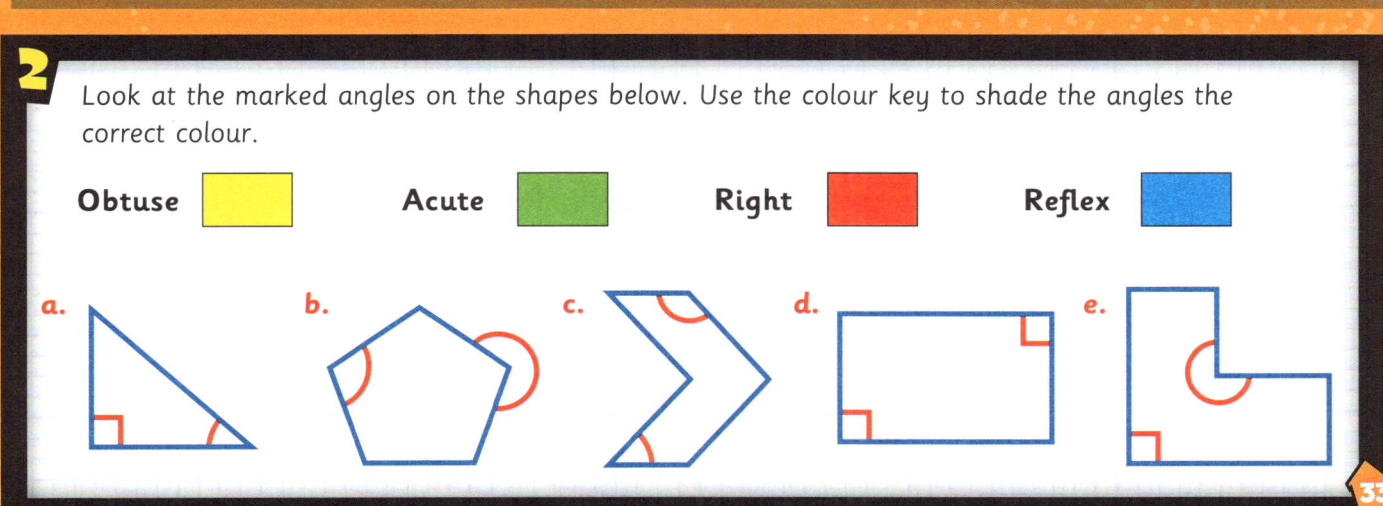

a.   b.   c.   d.   e.

MISSING ANGLES

Luan wants to work out the perfect angle to fire the water from her squirting flower. First, she needs to study the rules below which will help her work out the angles.

Angles on a straight line always add up to 180°.	The three internal angles of a triangle always add up to 180°.	Angles around a point always add up to 360°.	When two straight lines cross each other, the angles opposite each other are the same.
130° 50°	45° 90° 45°	240° 120°	100° 80° 80° 100°

(Angles not to scale)

1

Write the missing angles in the boxes below.

a.

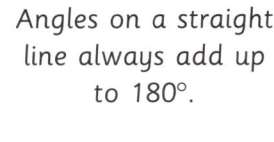

60°

b.

55° 82°

c.

116°

d.

70° 32°

e.

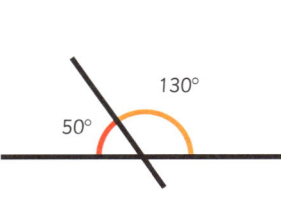

125°

f.

53°

g.

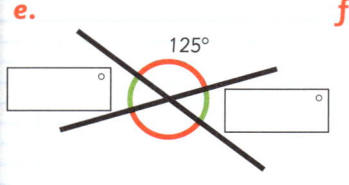

133° 30°

h.

81° 107°

(Angles not to scale)

2

Four angles meet together at a point.

One of the angles is a right angle.

One of the angles is 68°.

The two unknown angles are equal.

How many degrees are each of the unknown angles?

Have a go at drawing a rough diagram of the angles to prove your answer.

PROBABILITY

Lucy is very interested in the mystery of probability and has prepared some secret packages for her family. They each pick an item from one package. What will they receive?

Probability, which means the likelihood of something happening, can be expressed on a scale ranging from impossible to certain.

It is almost certain that Bobby will send at least 10 text messages to Lori each day.

1 Look at the pictures and circle how likely each event is to happen.

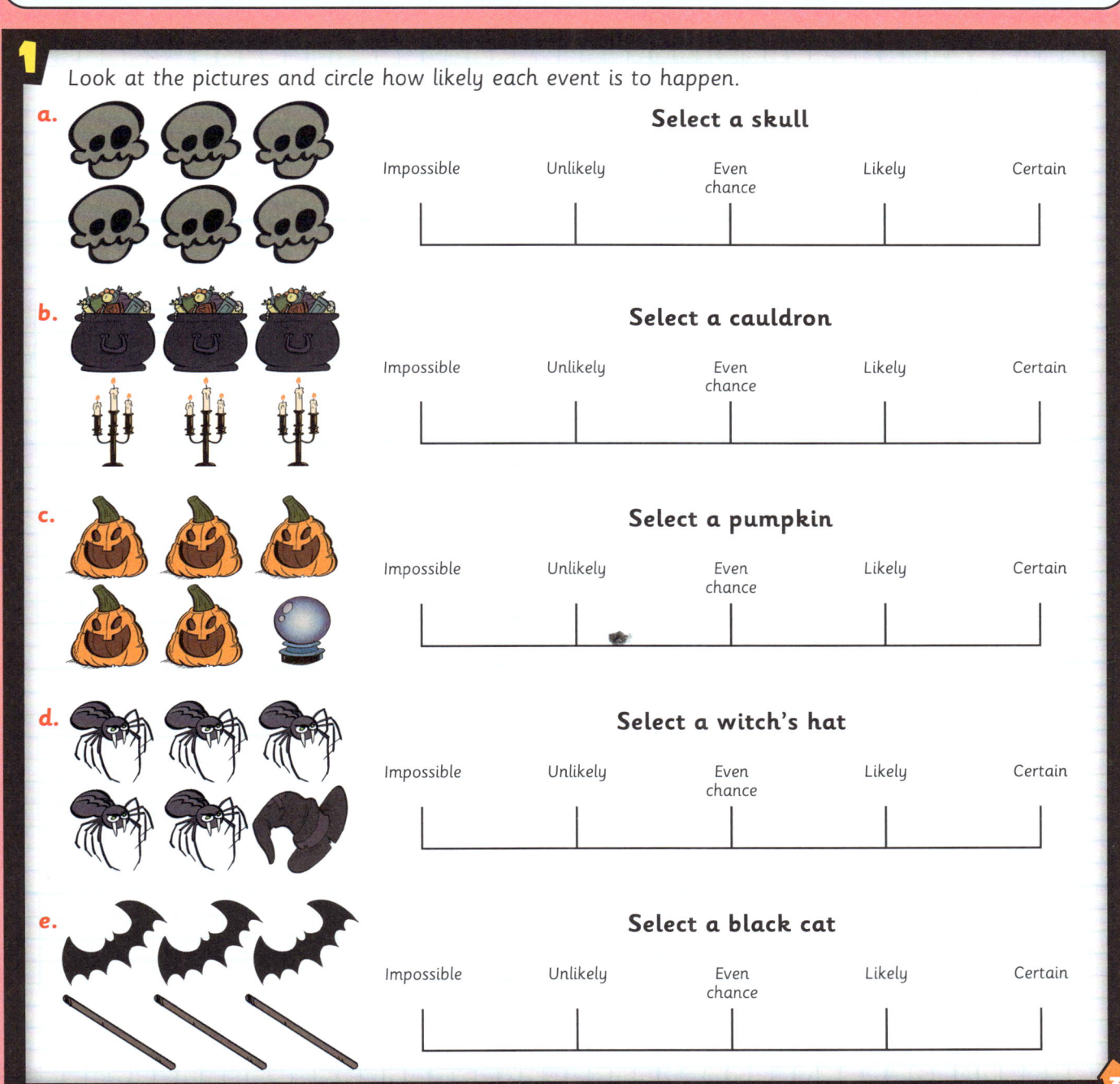

a. Select a skull

Impossible | Unlikely | Even chance | Likely | Certain

b. Select a cauldron

Impossible | Unlikely | Even chance | Likely | Certain

c. Select a pumpkin

Impossible | Unlikely | Even chance | Likely | Certain

d. Select a witch's hat

Impossible | Unlikely | Even chance | Likely | Certain

e. Select a black cat

Impossible | Unlikely | Even chance | Likely | Certain

PROBABILITY

As well as being measured on a scale, probability, or the likelihood of something happening, can be measured using fractions, decimals and percentages.

1

Lincoln and Clyde are playing a game using a spinner with numbers from 1 to 10. Can you work out how likely they are to land on the numbers described opposite and draw lines to the correct answers? The first one has been done for you.

a.	A nine.	$\frac{1}{2}$
b.	A red or yellow number.	$\frac{1}{10}$
c.	A number divisible by three.	0.3
d.	A number greater than 5.	40%
e.	A number less than 5.	20%
f.	A number greater than 3.	0.7

2 As a percentage, what is the probability that Clyde will spin a 1, 5 or 7?

3 As a fraction, what is the probability that Lincoln will spin a number divisible by 4?

4 As a decimal, what is the probability that Clyde will spin an even number?

COORDINATES

The Loud family have gone on their annual holiday to the Scratchy Bottom Campground.

1

Can you write down the coordinates of each black dot showing the locations of each of the children? The first one has been done for you. Use the last, empty space to add yourself to the grid and write the coordinates for your own location.

Remember, when you write and read coordinates, you take the x axis first and then the y axis.

So (3,5) means three across and then five up.

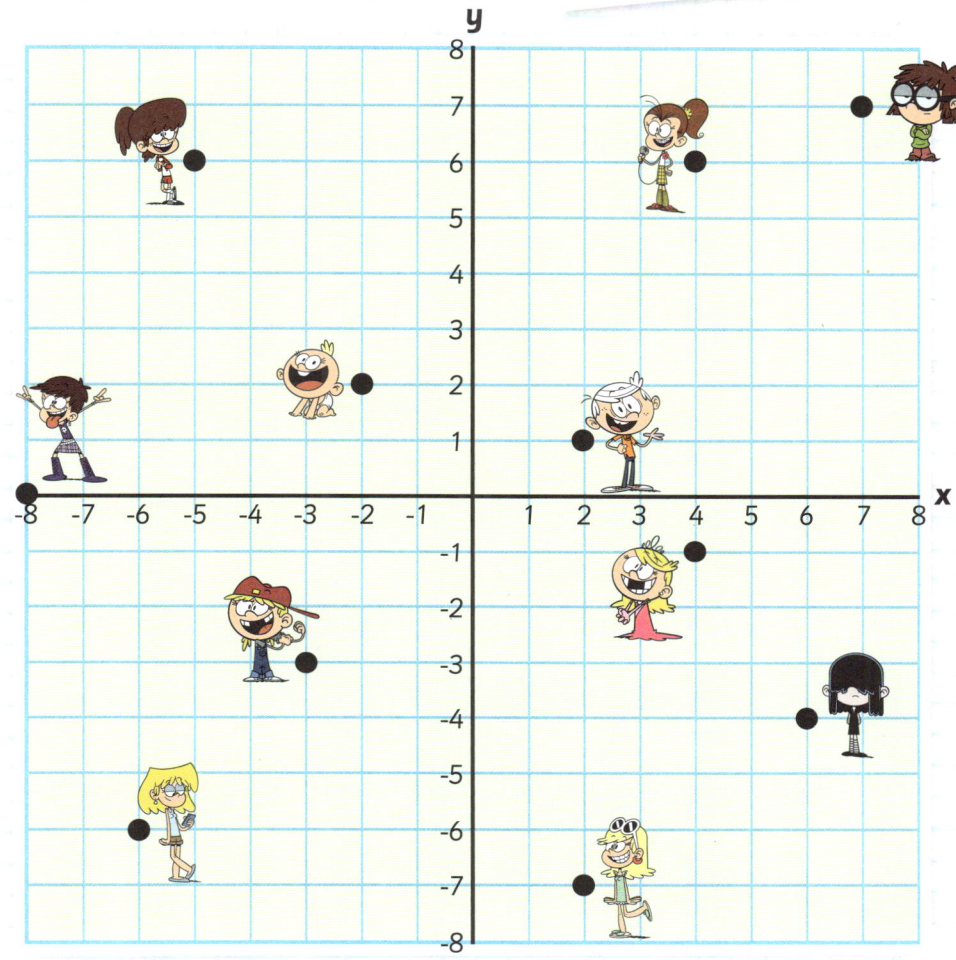

 **a.** Lily (-2, 2)   **b.** Lucy  (☐ , ☐)   **c.** Luna  (☐ , ☐)

d. Lisa  (☐ , ☐)   **e.** Lincoln  (☐ , ☐)   **f.** Leni  (☐ , ☐)

g. Lola  (☐ , ☐)   **h.** Lynn  (☐ , ☐)   **i.** Lori  (☐ , ☐)

j. Lana  (☐ , ☐)   **k.** Luan  (☐ , ☐)   **l.** _____ (☐ , ☐)

COORDINATES

Lynn Sr. and Rita have hidden some treasure at the campground for the siblings to find. Use the coordinates to find out where the treasure is hidden.

1

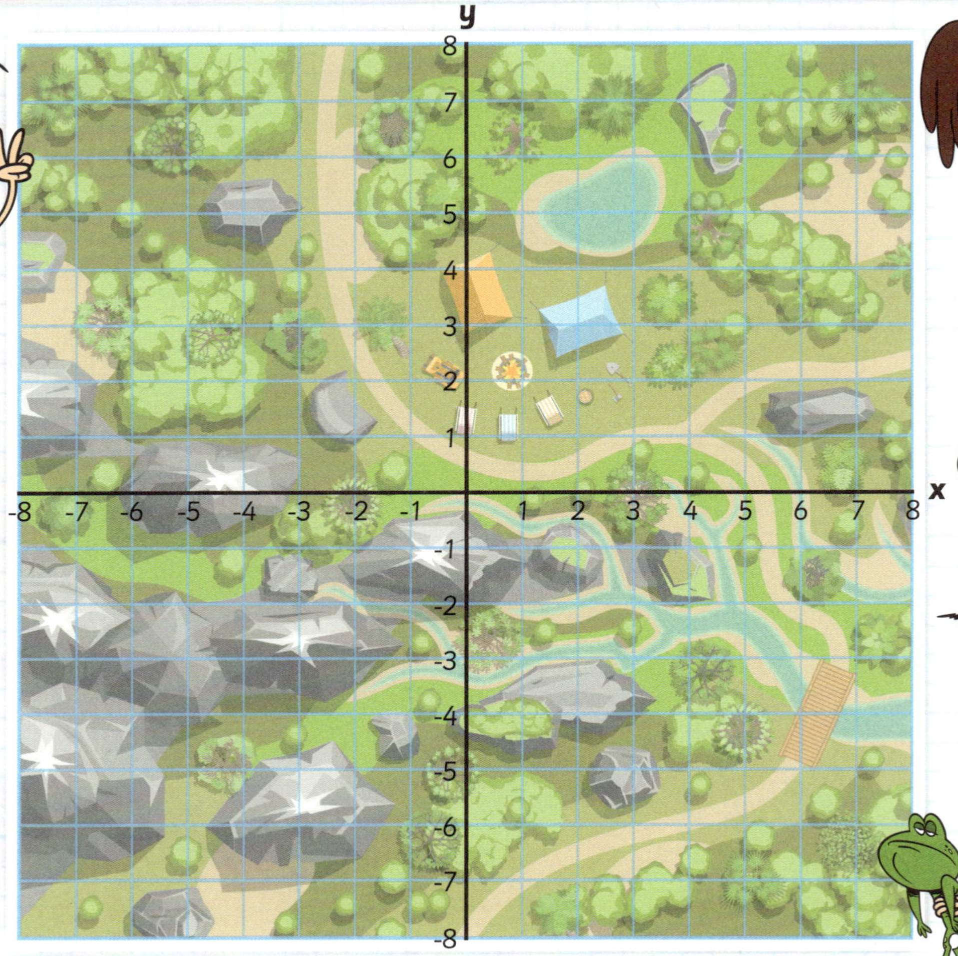

a. (1, 2)   Where is the treasure hidden?

b. (4, 7)   Where is the treasure hidden?

c. (0, -5)   Where is the treasure hidden?

d. (6, 1)   Where is the treasure hidden?

TRANSLATION

Leni is designing new wallpaper for her bedroom. She has selected pictures of a few of her favourite things and is using translation to place them repeatedly on the wallpaper.

> A translation is a type of transformation. It moves a shape up, down or from left to right, but it does not change its appearance in any other way.

1

Complete the sentences by filling in the gaps and crossing out the incorrect choices to show the translation Leni has used to go from shape a to b.

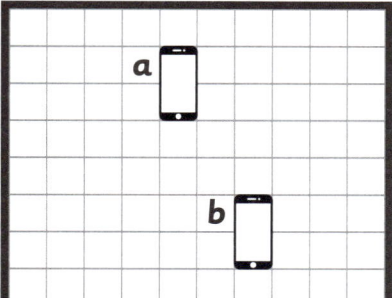 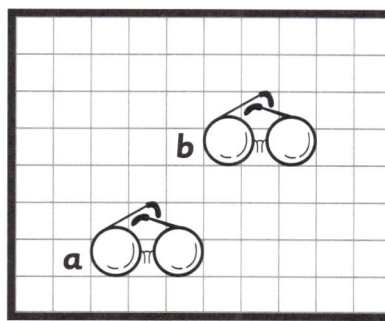 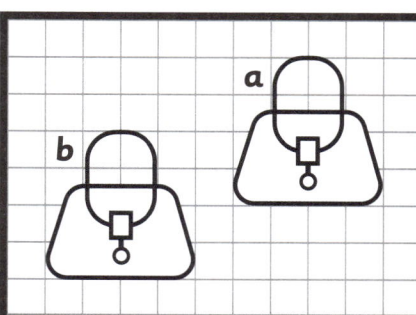

a. The phone has been translated ☐ squares to the left/right and ☐ squares up/down.

b. The sunglasses have been translated ☐ squares left/right and ☐ squares up/down.

c. The handbag has been translated ☐ squares left/right and ☐ squares up/down.

2

Complete the pattern by redrawing the shapes according to Leni's instructions.

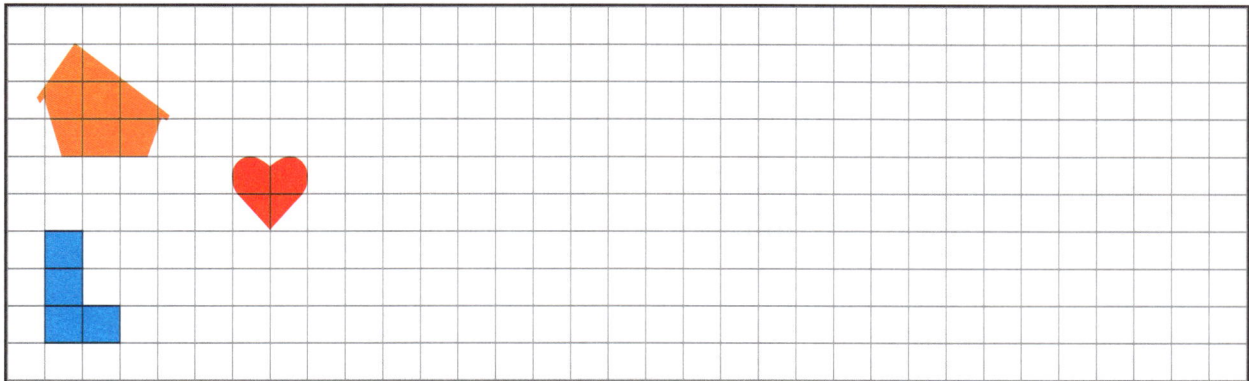

Translate the shapes as follows:

a. Translate the L 10 squares to the right and 3 squares up.

b. Translate the heart 3 squares to the right and 2 squares up.

c. Translate the house 6 squares to the right and 5 squares down.

REFLECTION

Lucy is investigating the mysteries of reflection, which is a type of transformation.

When an object is reflected, it needs a mirror line. The object's size doesn't change, the image just appears flipped so that every point on the shape is the same distance away on the other side of the mirror line.

1 Reflect the letters of Lucy's name in the mirror lines. The first one has been done for you.

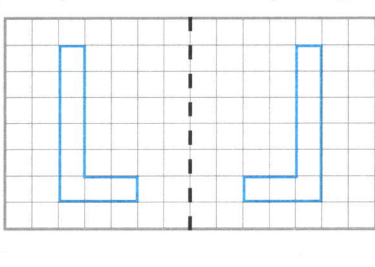
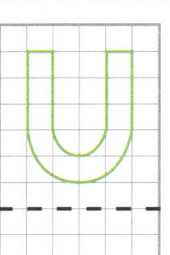
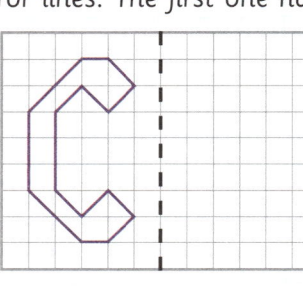
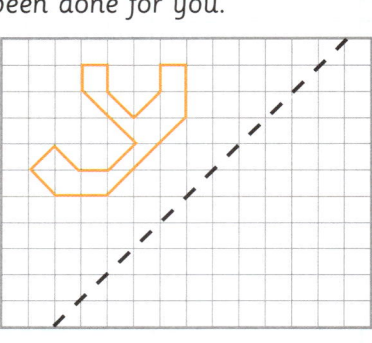

2 Lucy has a habit of popping up out of nowhere and making people jump. She's designed a cape to wear to make her sudden appearances even more mysterious! Can you shade the right side of the cape so that it's a reflection of the left side?

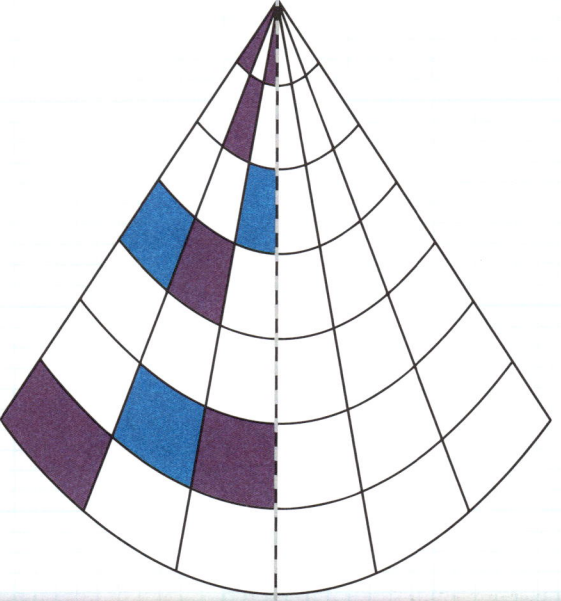

3 Lincoln is looking after the class pet, Frank. Look at the images of Frank below. Can you work out which are translations, which are reflections and which are neither?

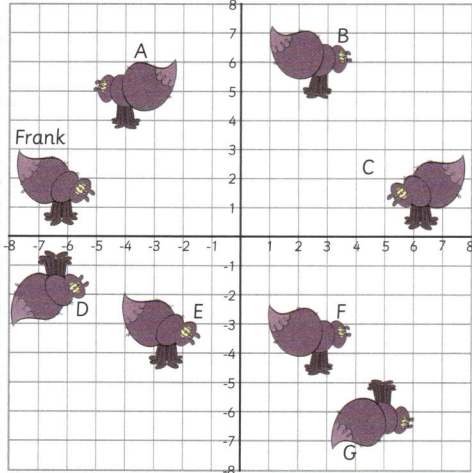

a. Translations:

b. Reflections:

c. Neither translations or reflections:

40

LINE GRAPHS

Luan wants to beat her sporty sister, Lynn, for once and has been using line graphs to keep track of her training.

How far Luan ran in a week

The horizontal (X) axis shows the days of the week and the vertical (Y) axis shows the distances. From the graph, you can see Luan ran the furthest on Sunday and the shortest distance on Friday.

1

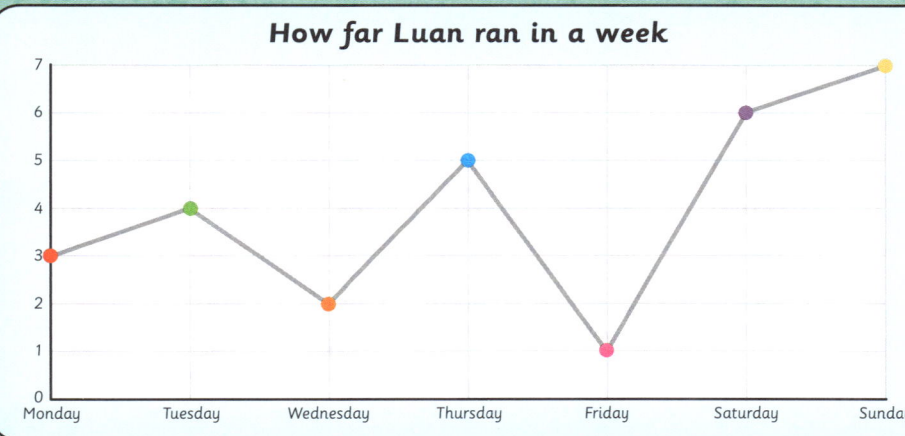

Number of bottle flips

Lynn's latest sport is bottle flipping so Luan has been practising her flips to try and beat her. This line graph shows the number of times Luan has made the bottle land correctly.

Look at the graph and use it to answer these questions.

a. On what day did she flip the greatest number of bottles?

b. On what day did she flip the least number of bottles?

c. On what days did she flip 4 bottles?

2

Luan and Lynn strike competition

— Lynn
— Luan

Luan has challenged Lynn to a bowling competition. This line graph shows the number of strikes each sister has scored over 10 weeks. Fill in the table below to work out who's scored the most and is the winner. The winner is _____.

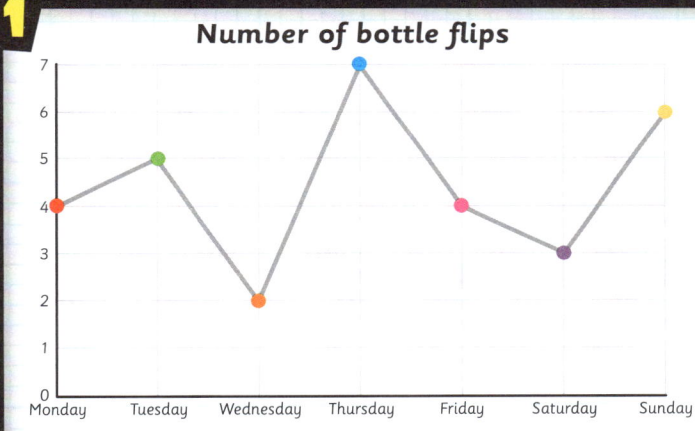

Week	Strikes - Lynn	Strikes – Luan
1	2	1
2		
3		
4		
5		
6		
7		
8		
9		
10		

TIMETABLES

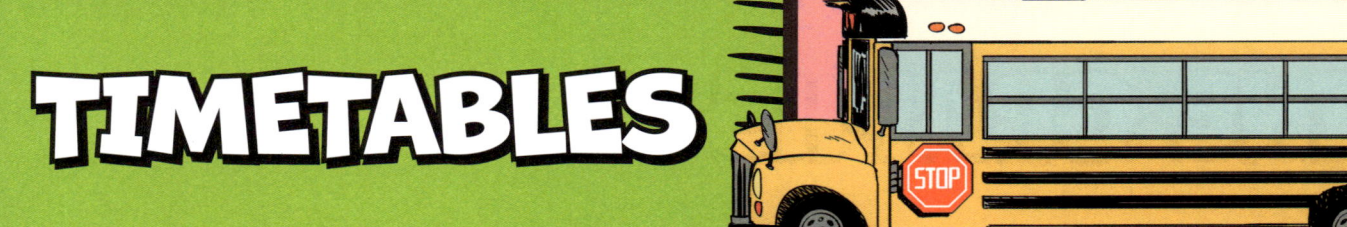

Royal Woods Bus Company has just updated its timetable for the school buses. Take a look at the timetable below and answer the questions.

School Bus Timetable					
Royal Woods Mall	06:45	07:00	07:15	07:20	07:42
Franklin Avenue	06:55	07:10	07:25	07:30	07:52
Lynn's Table	07:10	07:25	07:40	07:45	08:07
Royal Woods Baseball Stadium	07:20	07:35	07:50	07:55	08:17
Royal Woods Middle School	07:30	07:45	08:00	08:05	08:27

1

a. How long is the journey time in minutes from Royal Woods Mall to Lynn's Table?

b. If Lincoln arrived at school at 07:45 and got on the bus at Franklin Avenue, how long was he on the bus for?

c. What time does Lincoln need to be at Lynn's Table if he wants to get to school for 08:00?

d. How many minutes later is the next bus from Franklin Avenue after 07:20?

e. Lincoln says the longest time between stops is between Franklin Avenue and Lynn's Table. True or false?

f. Lincoln's friend Clyde says that if he boards the bus at 07:30 from Franklin Avenue, he will get to school at 08:27. True or false?

2

The return bus timetable is also being updated but it hasn't been finished yet. Can you complete it, using the timings from the first timetable to help you?

School Bus Timetable					
Royal Woods Middle School	14:55	15:00	15:10	15:20	
Royal Woods Baseball Stadium	15:05	15:10			15:45
Lynn's Table		15:20	15:30	15:40	15:55
Franklin Avenue	15:30	15:35	15:45		16:10
Royal Woods Mall	15:40		15:55	16:05	

TIMETABLES

After a wonderful summer kicking back with Clyde, Lincoln is wondering about his school timetable for the new year. He's written up an imaginary timetable with some new unusual school subjects.

1 Look at the timetable and answer the following questions.

	08:45 – 09:30	09:30 – 10:15	Break time (10:15 – 10:45)	10:45 – 11:45	Lunch (11:45 – 12:45)	12:45 – 13:45	13:45 – 14:45
Monday	English	Science		Maths		Library	Apothecary
Tuesday	Maths	Apothecary		English		Art	
Wednesday	English	Science		Maths		Fashion	Rock Music
Thursday	Maths	Fashion		English		Comedy Script Writing	
Friday	English	Rock Music		Maths		Science	Assembly

a. How many times a week does Lincoln have English?

b. How many hours does Comedy Script Writing last on a Thursday?

c. Which days does Maths start after Recess?

d. How many minutes are there of Recess each day?

2 Lincoln wants to fit in Comic Book studies to his imaginary timetable. To fit it in, Science needs to be moved. Use the information below to fill in the gaps on the timetable for Comic Book Studies and Science.

	08:45 – 09:30	09:30 – 10:15	Break time (10:15 – 10:45)	10:45 – 11:45	Lunch (11:45 – 12:45)	12:45 – 13:45	13:45 – 14:45
Monday	English			Math		Library	
Tuesday	Math	Geography		English		Art	
Wednesday	English	Computing		Math		Computing	History
Thursday	Math			English			
Friday	English	History		Math			Assembly

Comic Book Studies can only take place on a Monday, Thursday and Friday.
There can be no more than one session of Comic Book Studies in an afternoon per a week.
Science must be taught on a Monday and Thursday. Science must be for an hour on a Monday.
Overall, there should be 3 hours of Science.

PIE CHARTS

Lynn has taken part in lots of different sports this year. She is so competitive and just hates losing. Look at the pie charts below and complete the missing information.

1 Football Games Played

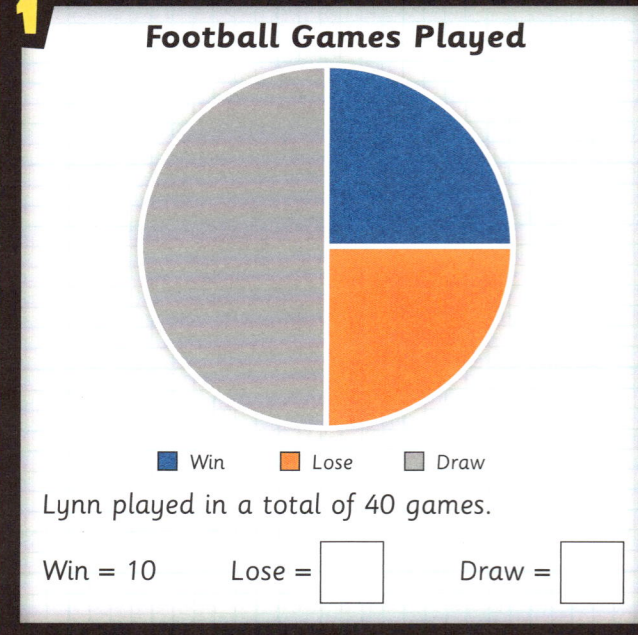

■ Win ■ Lose ■ Draw

Lynn played in a total of 40 games.

Win = 10   Lose = ☐   Draw = ☐

2 Basketball Games Played

■ Win ■ Lose ■ Draw

Lynn played in a total of 36 games.

Win = ☐   Lose = 6   Draw = ☐

3 Baseball Games

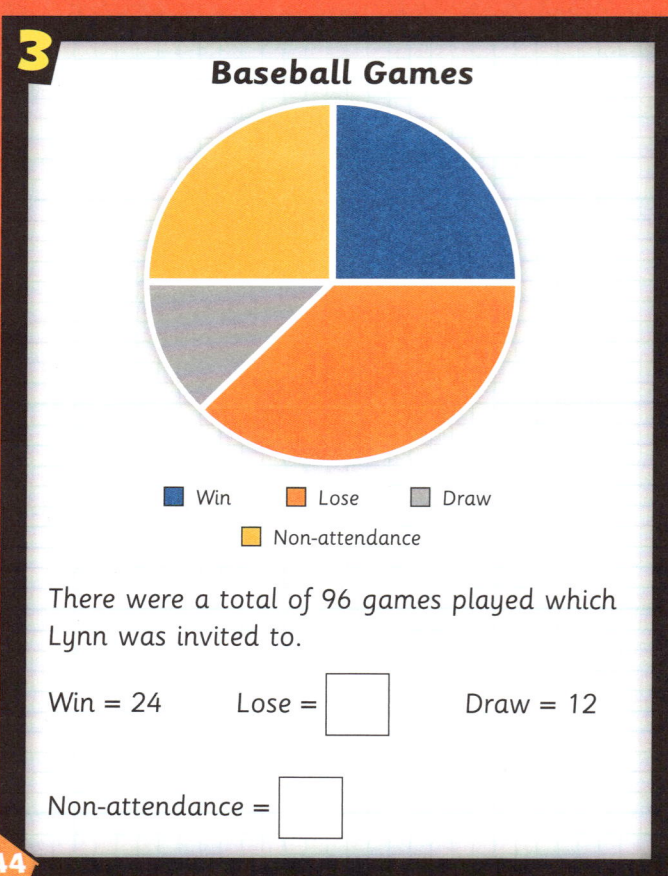

■ Win ■ Lose ■ Draw
■ Non-attendance

There were a total of 96 games played which Lynn was invited to.

Win = 24   Lose = ☐   Draw = 12

Non-attendance = ☐

4 Tennis Matches

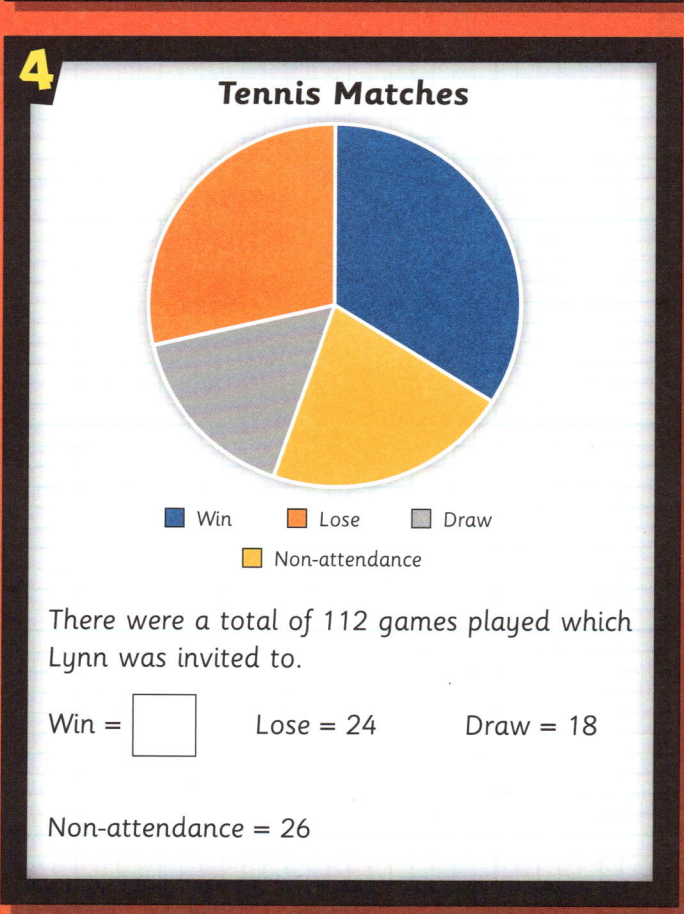

■ Win ■ Lose ■ Draw
■ Non-attendance

There were a total of 112 games played which Lynn was invited to.

Win = ☐   Lose = 24   Draw = 18

Non-attendance = 26

PIE CHARTS

Luan loves making people laugh! She's made some pie charts to show where the inspiration for her best jokes and pranks has come from and how her audience has reacted to them.

1

Look carefully at the pie chart and answer the questions below it.

Jokes and Pranks Ideas Influence

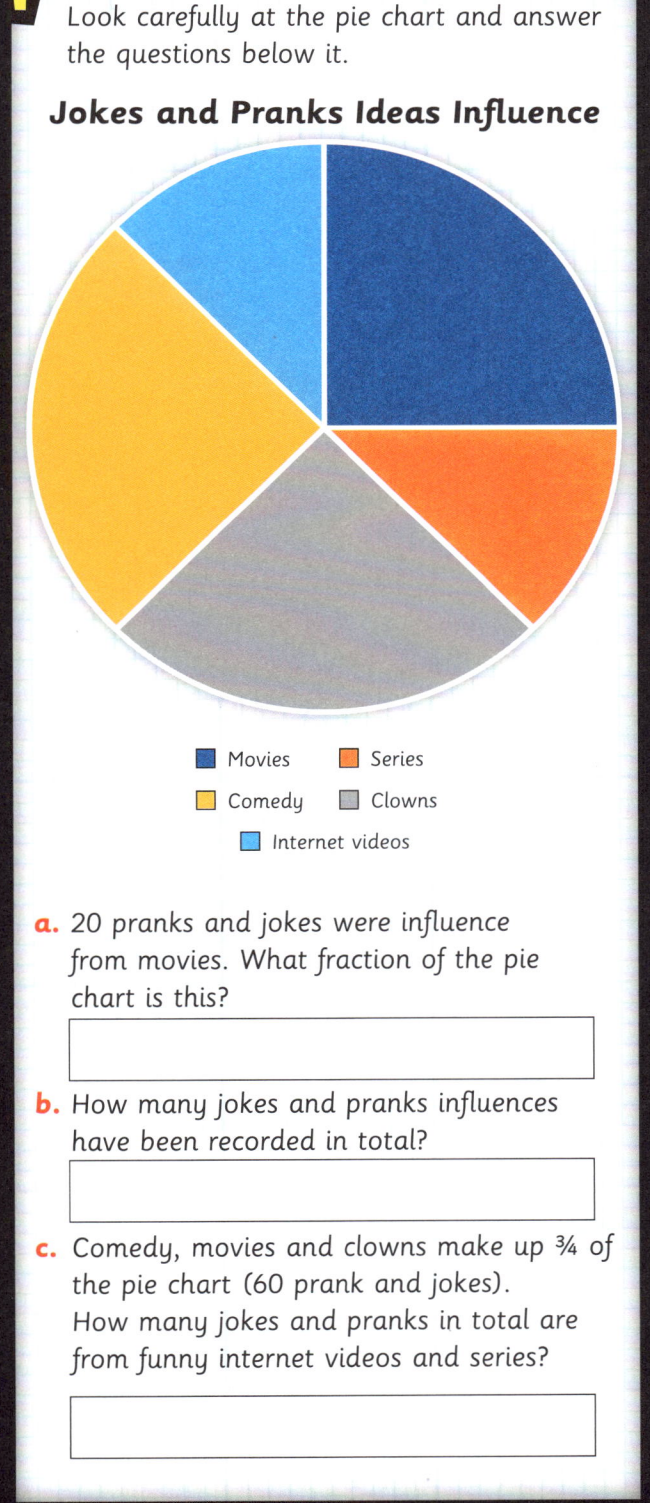

■ Movies ■ Series
■ Comedy ■ Clowns
■ Internet videos

a. 20 pranks and jokes were influence from movies. What fraction of the pie chart is this?

b. How many jokes and pranks influences have been recorded in total?

c. Comedy, movies and clowns make up ¾ of the pie chart (60 prank and jokes). How many jokes and pranks in total are from funny internet videos and series?

2

Look at this pie chart showing the prank and joke outcomes and answer the questions below.

Prank and Joke Outcomes

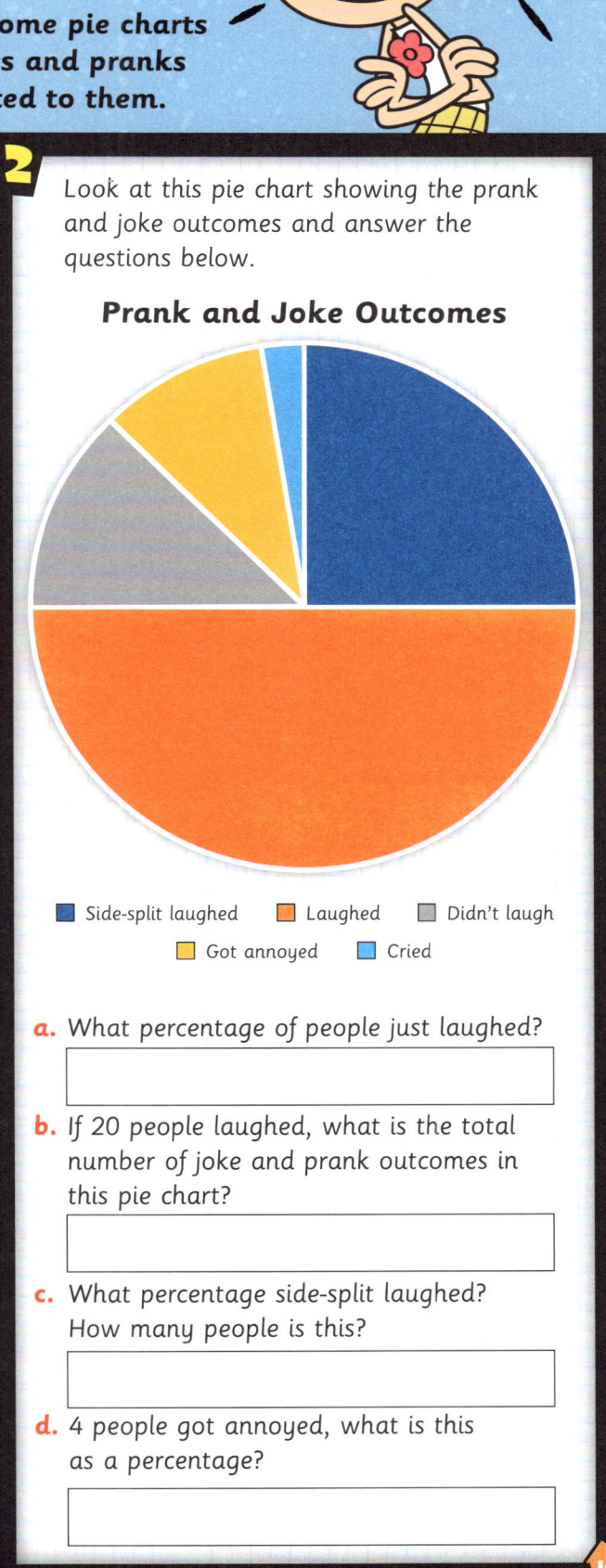

■ Side-split laughed ■ Laughed ■ Didn't laugh
■ Got annoyed ■ Cried

a. What percentage of people just laughed?

b. If 20 people laughed, what is the total number of joke and prank outcomes in this pie chart?

c. What percentage side-split laughed? How many people is this?

d. 4 people got annoyed, what is this as a percentage?

ANSWERS

Page 2: Numbers to 10,000,000
1. 60,000
   100,000
   700
   5,000,000
   7,000
   9
2. a. 5,655,345   d. 1,729,004
   b. 9,808,311   e. 9,909,900
   c. 2,446,651

Page 3: Rounding Numbers
1. 45 — 50, 32 — 30, 91 — 90,
   35 — 40, 75 — 80
2. 256, 309, 299
3. 8,008, 8,080, 8,401
4. 49,356, 45,001, 48,743
5. a. 60 and 100
   b. 600 and 1000
   c. 7,000 and 10,000
   d. 70,000 and 100,000

Page 4: Problem Solving
1. a. 1,252,869   c. 1,552,869
   b. 1,252,899   d. 1,252,872
2. a. 9,865,221
   b. 1,225,689
   c. Possibilities: 52,829, 52,629,
      62,529, 62,829

Page 5: Negative Numbers
1.

	4pm temperature	Best for sledging? 4 or 6
Mon	(4 - 8 = -4) -4°C	4
Tue	(7 – 6 = 1) 1°C	6
Wed	(1 – 3 = -2) -2°C	4
Thur	(-1 – 1 = -2) -2°C	4

Wednesday, Thursday and Friday
are the best days for sledging.
2. b. =2, =, =2   d. =-4, <, =-1
   c. =1, >, =-1   e. =-4, =, =-4

Page 6: Roman Numerals
1. a. LXXX   d. CMXC
   b. DI   e. XVIII
   c. XCIV
2. a. CXXXIV   e. 571
   b. DCCCIV   f. 29
   c. 770   g. DLIV
   d. 362   h. DCCCLXXX
3. MCCLVI, MCDXLI, MDCC, MDCCCV,
   MMXXII

Page 7: Addition
1. a. 5888 b. 8668 c. 4222 d. 8023
   e. 8790 f. 5831 g. 8622
2. a.

```
    4  3  2  5
 +  2  6  3  6
 ──────────────
    6  9  6  1
```

b.

```
          1
    5  1  2  1
 +  2  1  8  3
 ──────────────
    7  3  0  4
```

c.

```
          1
    4  4  5  8
 +  3  5  8  8
 ──────────────
    8  0  4  6
    1  1  1
```

Page 8: Subtraction
1. a. 6443   c. 4869   e. 1506
   b. 3111   d. 3317   f. 5357
2. a. Lori

```
    ⁵6̸ ¹¹7̸ ¹1  5
 -   3  8  3  3
 ──────────────
     2  3  8  2
```

b. Lori

```
    7  5  ³6̸ ¹4
 -  2  4  1  9
 ──────────────
    5  1  2  5
```

c. Bobby

```
   ¹2̸ ¹6̸ ³4̸ ¹8
 -      8  2  9
 ──────────────
    1  8  1  9
```

Page 9: Mental Addition and Subtraction
1. a. True   b. False   c. True.
   d. True   e. True
2. a. 129   b. 210   c. 309
   d. 120   e. 724   f. 930

Page 10: Mental Addition and Subtraction
1. b. 30   e. 105   h. 75
   c. 20   f. 46   i. 142
   d. 115 g. 12   j. 135
2. a. 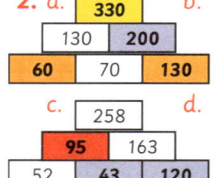   b.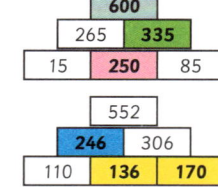
   c.

```
          258
    95    163
  52   43   120
```

   d.

```
          552
    246   306
  110   136   170
```

Page 11: Addition and Subtraction
1. Luna has (£50 + £20 + £85.20) =
   £155.20.
   £155.20 – £135 = £20.20
   Luna can afford the guitar and
   would have £20.20 left over.
2. 130km + (130km x 2) + 37km =
   427km.
   500km – 427km = 73km.
   73 – 15 = 58km. They will have
   58km worth of petrol to spare.
3. Beaker A: 270ml + 323ml = 593ml
   Beaker B: 180ml + 135ml = 315ml
   Difference between the two beakers
   (593ml - 315ml) = 278ml.
4. Total minutes delivery/lifeguard/
   security (235mins + 380mins +
   220mins) = 835 minutes.
   Remaining working time
   (1250mins – 835mins) = 415mins
   He has spent 415 minutes as a
   grocery stock boy.

Page 12: Prime Numbers
1. The prime numbers are: 2, 11, 29,
   37, 47
2. a. 53 and 59   d. 83 and 89
   b. 61 and 67   e. 97
   c. 71, 73 and 79
3. a. 5 and 3   b. 17 and 11
   c. 13 and 2   d. 19 and 2

Page 13: Written Multiplication
1. a. 738   b. 796   c. 802   d. 750
   e. 1590 f. 2863 g. 4290 h. 2936
2. a. 1395 b. 2055 c. 1448 d. 5496.

Page 14: Written Multiplication
1. a.

x	20	4	
10	200	40	240
9	180	36	+216
			456

b.

x	30	5	
40	1200	200	1400
3	90	15	+105
			1505

c.

x	30	6	
20	600	120	720
5	150	30	+180
			900

d.

x	60	6	
30	1800	180	1980
3	180	18	+198
			2178

2. a.
```
      3 4          c.       3 4
    x 2 1              x 1 9
      3 4              3 0 6
    6 8 0            3 4 0
    7 1 4            6 4 6
```
b.
```
      2 3
    x 2 2
      4 6
    4 6 0
    5 0 6
```

Page 15: Written Division
1. a. 142 b. 77r4 c. 70r7 d. 107r4
2. a.1302r1 b. 504r3 c. 2672 d. 333r6
3. a. 9 b. 5 c. 5 d. r8

Page 16: Written Division
1. a.
```
         0   1   2   3
    12 | 1   4   7   6
         1   2
             2   7
             2   4
                 3   6
                 3   6
                     0
```
b.
```
         0   1   4   5
    12 | 1   7   4   0
         1   2
             5   4
             4   8
                 6   0
                 6   0
                     0
```
c.
```
         0   1   5   5
    12 | 1   8   6   0
         1   2
             6   6
             6   0
                 6   0
                 6   0
                     0
```
d.
```
             3   1   2
    12 | 3   7   4   4
         3   6
             1   4
             1   2
                 2   4
                 2   4
                     0
```

Page 17: Fractions
1.

Mixed number fraction	Improper fraction
$3\frac{1}{4}$	$\frac{13}{4}$
$2\frac{5}{8}$	$\frac{21}{8}$
$4\frac{4}{6}$ or $4\frac{2}{3}$	$\frac{28}{6}$ or $\frac{14}{3}$
$2\frac{2}{3}$	$\frac{8}{3}$

2. a. $\frac{11}{3}$ c. $\frac{13}{2}$ e. $\frac{25}{6}$
   b. $\frac{18}{7}$ d. $\frac{27}{5}$ f. $\frac{31}{4}$
3. a. $2\frac{2}{3}$ c. $3\frac{2}{5}$ e. $5\frac{1}{4}$
   b. $2\frac{5}{6}$ d. $9\frac{1}{2}$ f. $3\frac{1}{7}$

Page 18: Adding Fractions
1. a. $\frac{7}{6}$ b. $\frac{19}{10}$ c. $\frac{7}{4}$ d. $\frac{37}{8}$
2. a. $\frac{5}{6}$ b. $\frac{13}{10}$ c. $\frac{7}{12}$
   d. $\frac{13}{10}$ e. $\frac{27}{20}$ f. $\frac{19}{15}$
3. a. $\frac{17}{6}$ b. $\frac{46}{12}$ or $\frac{23}{6}$
   c. $\frac{30}{10}$ or $\frac{3}{1}$ d. $\frac{28}{10}$ or $\frac{14}{5}$
   e. $\frac{90}{20}$ or $\frac{45}{10}$ f. $\frac{47}{15}$

Page 19: Subtracting Fractions
1. a. $\frac{13}{8}$ b. $\frac{5}{2}$ c. $\frac{8}{4}$ d. $\frac{8}{3}$
2. a. $\frac{19}{6}$ or $\frac{38}{12}$ b. $\frac{22}{20}$ or $\frac{11}{10}$
   c. $\frac{22}{15}$ d. $\frac{12}{10}$ or $\frac{6}{5}$
3. b. $\frac{48}{6} - \frac{27}{6} = \frac{21}{6}$ or $\frac{7}{2}$ >3
   c. $\frac{27}{6} - \frac{12}{6} = \frac{15}{6}$ or $\frac{5}{2}$ >1
   d. $\frac{40}{10} - \frac{24}{10} = \frac{16}{10}$ or $\frac{8}{5}$ <2
   e. $\frac{28}{12} - \frac{6}{12} = \frac{22}{12}$ or $\frac{11}{6}$ >1
   f. $\frac{35}{15} - \frac{3}{15} = \frac{32}{15}$ or   >2

Page 20: Multiplying Fractions
1. b. $\frac{1}{5}$ c. $\frac{1}{4}$ d. $\frac{18}{35}$ e. $\frac{2}{27}$
2. $\frac{2}{2}$ = 1 pizza
   $\frac{12}{6}$ = 2 pizzas
   $\frac{12}{8}$ = 1 pizza and $\frac{1}{2}$ pizza

Page 21: Ordering Fractions
1. a. $\frac{1}{8}$ | $\frac{1}{4}$ | 0.5 | $\frac{7}{10}$ | $\frac{3}{4}$ | 0.8
   b. 0.1 | $\frac{1}{9}$ | $\frac{2}{8}$ | $\frac{1}{3}$ | $\frac{5}{10}$ | $\frac{10}{12}$
   c. 0.4 | $\frac{1}{2}$ | 0.7 | $1\frac{1}{4}$ | $\frac{10}{5}$ | $2\frac{2}{3}$
   d. $\frac{1}{8}$ | 0.25 | 0.3 | $\frac{9}{6}$ | $1\frac{3}{4}$ | $\frac{7}{2}$

Page 22: Ratio and Proportion
1. a. 2 out of 10, 2:8, 1:4
   b. 3 out of 8, 3:5.
   c. 6 out of 8, 6:2, 3:1
2. a.
b.
c.

Page 23: Percentages
1. a. 50   e. 30   i. 20
   b. 25   f. 70   j. 10
   c. 10   g. 100 k. 60
   d. 5   h. 50   l. 140
2. b. £60 — £12.00 — £48.00
   c. £50 — £7.50 — £42.50
   d. £85 — £4.25 — £80.75
   e. £100 — £30.00 — £70.00

Page 24: Scale Factors
1. a. 2 b. 4 c. 5, 30cm d. 3, 30cm
2.

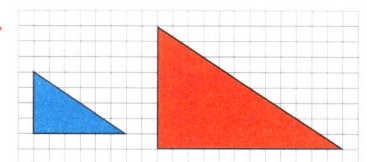

Page 25: Simple Formula
1. b. y = 15   c. n = 15   d. x = 10
   e. y = 5   f. x = 36
2. b. a = 4   c. n = 9   d. c = 3
   e. n = 45 f. x = 10 g. c = 5
   h. a = 8   i. n = 5

Page 26: Number Sequences

Tue	Wed	Thur	Fri	Sat	Sun
8	14	20	26	32	38
2 minutes	4 minutes	8 minutes	16 minutes	32 minutes	64 minutes
35 minutes	28 minutes	21 minutes	14 minutes	7 minutes	0 minutes
5	11	23	47	95	191
8	26	80	242	728	2186
12	32	72	152	312	632
310 seconds (5 mins 10 secs)	150 seconds (2 mins 30 secs)	70 seconds (1 min 10 secs)	30 seconds	10 seconds	0 seconds

Page 27: Algebra Word Problems
1. a. d = 7w + 3   b. 59 days
2. a. c = 12b + 25s   d. 3 sequin
   b. yes   badges
   c. £1.20
3. a. tp = 1820   b. £1.40
4. packs now = p/2 +3. He had 18 packs.

Page 28: Converting Units of Measurement
1. Lana is correct **3.** Lola is correct
2. Lola is correct **4.** Lana is correct
5. a. 35cm, 350mm, 0.35m
   b. 0.4kg, 400g,
   c. 14cl, 140ml, 0.14l
   d. 1560kg, 1.56 tonnes, 1560000g

Page 29: Perimeter

1. a. 24m   b. 26m   c. 26m
   d. 32m   e. 26m   f. 30m
   g. 20m   h. 24m   i. 30m

Page 30: Calculating Area

1. a. 36m²   b. 30m²   c. 30m²
   d. 28m²   e. 26m²   f. 30m²
   g. 16m²   h. 15m²   i. 17m²

2. a. 0.84m²   d. 0.56m²   g. 0.33m²
   b. 0.12m²   e. 0.34m²   h. 0.28m²
   c. 0.28m²   f. 0.35m²

Page 31: Calculating Area

1. There are 18 possibilities.

2. Width + length must equal half of the perimeter. Then there must be half of this number of possibilities e.g. if perimeter was 16m, width + length must equal 8. The possibilities are 1 & 8, 2 & 7, 3 & 6, 4 & 4. This makes 4 possibilities (same as half the width + length).

3. a. 18m by 18m   b. 324m²

4. 7m by 29m and 10m by 26m

Page 32: Miles and Kilometres

1. 1.6km, 8km, 7.2km, 14.4km, 20km

2. 7 miles, 6.5 miles, 6 miles, 10 miles, 3.5 miles

3. >, =, >, >, =

Page 33: Angles

1. a. acute angle   c. reflex angle
   b. right angle   d. obtuse angle
   e. right angle

2.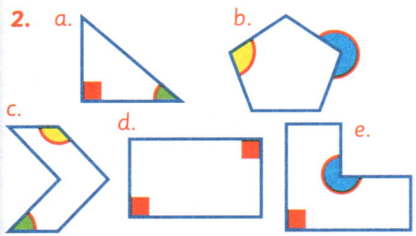

Page 34: Missing Angles

1. a. 120°   d. 78°   g. 47°, 343°
   b. 43°   e. 55°, 55°   h. 99°, 73°
   c. 154°   f. 37°

2. 360° - 90 = 270
   270 − 68 = 202
   202 ÷ 2 = 101

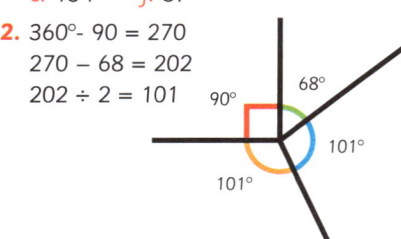

Page 35: Probability

1. a. Certain   d. Unlikely
   b. Even chance   e. Impossible
   c. Likely

Page 36: Probability

1. b. 20%   d. $\frac{1}{2}$ f. 0.7
   c. 0.3   e. 40%

2. 30%

3. $\frac{2}{10}$ or $\frac{1}{5}$

4. 0.5

Page 37: Coordinates

1. a. (-2,2)   b. (6,-4)   c. (-8,0)
   d. (7,7)   e. (2,1)   f. (2,-7)
   g. (4,-1)   h. (-5,6)   i. (-6,-6)
   j. (-3,-3)   k. (4,6)

Page 38: Coordinates

1. a.   c.
   b.   d.

Page 39: Translation

1. a. 2 right, 4 down
   b. 3 right, 3 up
   c. 5 left, 2 down

2.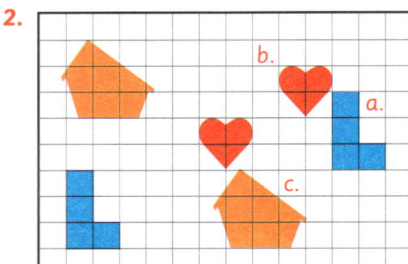

Page 40: Reflection

1.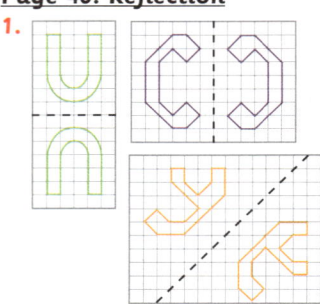

2.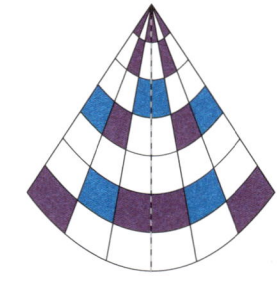

3. a. B, E, F   b. C, D   c. A, G

Page 41: Line Graphs

1. a. Thursday   c. Monday & Friday
   b. Wednesday

2.

Week	Strikes – Lynn	Strikes – Luan
1	2	1
2	3	2
3	5	5
4	2	3
5	6	0
6	2	0
7	0	4
8	1	2
9	2	6
10	7	4

The winner is Lynn.

Page 42: Timetables

1. a. 25 minutes   d. 5 minutes
   b. 35 minutes   e. True
   c. 07:40   f. False

2. Royal Woods Middle School - 15:35
   Royal Woods Baseball Stadium - 15:20, 15:30
   Lynn's Table - 15:15
   Franklin Avenue - 15:55
   Royal Woods Mall - 15:45, 16:20

Page 43: Timetables

1. a. 5
   b. 2 hours
   c. Monday, Wednesday and Friday
   d. 30 minutes

2.

	09:30 – 10:15	12:45 – 13:45	13:45 – 14:45
Mon	Comic Book Studies	Library	Science
Tues	Geography	Art	
Wed	Computing	Computing	History
Thur	Comic Book Studies	Science	Science
Fri	History	Comic Book Studies	Assembly

Page 44: Pie Charts

1. Lose: 10   Draw: 20
2. Win: 18   Draw: 12
3. Lose: 36   Non-attendance: 24
4. Win: 44

Page 45: Pie Charts

1. a. $\frac{1}{4}$ b. 80   c. 20

2. a. 50%   b. 40   c. 25%, 10   d. 10%